ST. CHR...
IN CELEBRATION

ST. CHRISTOPHER'S IN CELEBRATION

Twenty-one years at Britain's first modern hospice

Edited by

CICELY SAUNDERS

HODDER AND STOUGHTON
LONDON SYDNEY AUCKLAND TORONTO

British Library Cataloguing in Publication Data

St Christopher's in celebration: twenty-one years
   at Britain's first modern hospice.
   1. London. Lewisham (London Borough). Sydenham.
   Hospices: St Christopher's Hospice
   I. Saunders, *Dame*, Cicely
   362.1′75

ISBN 0-340-50841-8

Contents

Acknowledgments

The following chapters first appeared in the *Nursing Times* on the dates indicated: Chapter 1 (March 31st, 1961); Chapter 14 (June 22nd 1980); Chapters 16 and 17 (July 21st, 1982).

Chapter 3 first appeared in *On Dying Well: an Anglican contribution to the debate on euthanasia*, Church Information Office, London, 1975.

Chapter 6 is based on a BBC *Thought for the Day* programme.

The poems in Chapter 7 first appeared in *In a Lifetime*, JNR Publishing, New York, 1975.

Chapter 11 is adapted from a contribution to *New Meanings of Death*, ed. Herman Feifel, McGraw-Hill, New York, 1977.

Some of Sidney Reeman's poems in Chapter 10 have appeared in *Beyond All Pain*, edited by Cicely Saunders, SPCK, 1983.

The quotation from Judge Patrick Devlin at the end of Chapter 21 comes from his book *Easing the Passing; the trial of Dr John Bodkin Adams*, Bodley Head, 1985.

The following chapters first appeared in the Annual Report of St. Christopher's Hospice in the years indicated: Chapter 8 (1973–4); Chapters 12 and 13 (1976–7); Chapter 14 'Panacea' (1979–80); Chapter 18 (1982–3); Chapter 19 (1984–5); Chapter 22 (1986–7).

Introduction

Cicely Saunders

St. Christopher's Hospice opened its doors in July 1967. No better way could be found to celebrate these first twenty-one years of Britain's first modern hospice than to present the stories of twenty-one of our many thousand patients. Their needs and their achievements have been the centre and the stimulus for all the development of these years. But they would not have been free to find and express their true selves and to remain close to their families for the last part of their lives had it not been for the awareness and skills of the various members of staff; so we celebrate them also.

Before turning to the twenty-one stories from within St. Christopher's I have to include my own tribute to a patient whose friendship was a great inspiration and support to me during the long years of preparation. I knew her for the seven years of her illness and she helped me through the years when I was plodding my way through a full medical training in order to work in the field of controlling terminal pain. She also discussed many of the ideas that finally crystallised in the plans for a new hospice. She is truly one of our founders and she has to be here. It was she who gave us our name. When I explained that hospice meant 'resting place for travellers' she said 'Travelling? Well, you'll have to have St. Christopher, won't you.'

I have taken the other stories from entries in our annual reports and from other publications contributed to by members of our staff. They have not been altered, and show the impact that each patient and family made upon the writers at the time. I have also included contributions by patients themselves – a drawing, two sets of poems and an article – all written by people struggling to find the real meaning of their illnesses. Finally, there are memories from family members giving their own salute to those they loved. All the families I have been able to reach have asked for the names of their loved ones to be given in full. The rest are represented, as they were originally, by initials or pseudonyms. So the story of twenty-one years is told by focusing on these varied accounts, from the main points of view to be considered in any hospice development, those of patients, families and staff. Nor have we forgotten our frail and elderly members in the Drapers' Wing. Their contribution to the faith and stability of the Hospice family is well illustrated in the story of two of its early residents.

The majority of the patients whose stories are told here – like those many thousands they represent – were sent to St. Christopher's for help in the control of symptoms, especially for the control of pain. The pain suffered by many patients with terminal cancer was well defined some fifty years ago by Professor R. Leriche when he wrote, 'Pain is the resultant of the conflict between a stimulus and the whole individual.' A hospice team, whether working in a patient's own home, a day centre or with in-patient beds, tries to be aware of such pain and is thus concerned with all aspects of the person and the whole group of people involved with the patient.

A hospice team neither hastens death nor prolongs dying but sets out to enhance the quality of the life that remains once active treatment can no longer offer control of the disease process. Appropriate limited treatment continues, with the aim of palliating symptoms. Over the past twenty years this has become better understood, more widely taught and practised. Part of St. Christopher's commitment has been to carry out some of the research that has been the objective foundation of this teaching. Now it is estimated that some 40,000 of the 140,000 who die of cancer in the United Kingdom each year have some contact with a hospice, or a support or continuing care team, either at home or in a general hospital or in a special unit. At the same time the same principles and skills are spreading through the whole field of general medicine.

In controlling physical distress we aim for our patient's independence, even where that may present the problems of an obstinate loner like Sam; we try to maintain due regard for appearance and self-esteem for people like Paula, and indeed for everything that keeps going something of normal life. We try to enable patients to remain at home as long as possible – perhaps to the end, as for Mrs Barton and Brian – but admission is available when caring becomes too heavy. Mrs Williams's comment, 'unhampered by physical caring, we could be quiet *together*', describes what can be offered in a short-term final admission. It will, I think, be obvious that the control of symptoms is not gained at the expense of the patient's personality or alertness. For a very few, like Mr Soames, it may mean back to normal living again.

We have to listen to the details of symptoms, giving constant attention to changing needs. We are concerned both to relieve suffering and that our patients should maintain their own character and style to the end. Very few have such an internal struggle in the last hours as George, the fighter in the night, but patients are referred to a hospice because of problems that other people have found difficult to control and the whole team has to be constantly on the alert and ready to help in this as well as in meeting all practical needs. All the other patients in this group died peacefully – as he did, too, in the end.

We may have continually to alter drugs and their combinations, as we did for Brian, Paula, Gabby and some of the others. We do not find that with our regime of giving drugs regularly to prevent pain from recurring we need constantly to increase the dose. Pain killers maintain their effect and it is only rarely that large doses are needed. To illustrate: in 1985 the maximum dose of morphine given to 80 per cent of all our patients was at a regular 'post-operative' level or less. Only 5 per cent received what could be considered large doses. The idea that hospices carry out a regular increase of dose to the end can be shown by statistics to be untrue. A few patients are like Sam and may resist the drugs that could have helped them as a kind of declaration of independence. That, too, has to be recognised and honoured as Sam's story shows.

Concern for 'family pain' is well illustrated in two of the longer contributions: the story of John and his gradual coming to terms, and the description of the final letting-go by George during that last long night. Even young families like Joan's can come to accept and grow from the devastating loss of a mother where there has been time to share what is happening, make plans and say farewell. Sometimes we have to help patients assert their place in the group as they all become aware of their resources and strengths. The Hospice does not force truth upon people who are not ready for it, but sets out to give enough security for communication to open up so that sharing can happen and informed choices be made. We are trying to help people to be as honest as they can, to find reconciliation when it is needed and to say goodbye. We would not think of setting out on any other journey without a word of farewell and, although love often has no need of words and we do not impose our judgments upon others, real sharing at this time has a quality that can crown a relationship. Susie needed to emerge from her long silences to leave very special memories with her mother; and one wife recalls, 'Looking back I am glad we struggled through the Slough of Despond even though it was very painful – it was at least very honest. I am grateful that through the pain we were able to reach such a deep level of understanding.'

I have written briefly of pain of the body and of pain in the family but beyond both of those we have recognised pain of the mind and spirit. All four of the patients who have contributed battled their way through this and although, as Ted writes, 'It is a day-to-day effort to adjust and adapt to a declining capability' and not a once-for-all decision, yet their progress into greater acceptance and peace is clear. As he travelled his own journey Ted himself was a real friend, confidant and supporter of numerous members of the Hospice staff. His room was always welcoming and I treasured my visits and discussion with him over the years he was in the Hospice and missed him deeply as did many others.

The realisation that life is likely to end soon, whether or not it is faced openly, stimulates many to set out to put right what is wrong, though some may feel unable or even unworthy to do so. There may be bitter anger at what is happening, or at much of what has gone before, and above all a desolating feeling of meaninglessness. The Hospice has tried to be a place where these problems can be faced and resolved in a fully personal way.

Most of us have a desire to belong safely to something greater than our own insecure and vulnerable selves. The search for a meaning to things that includes oneself has recently been shown to be the major concern of a group of hospitalised patients. In a 1986 nursing research study Barbara Simsen found that their beliefs were important to two-thirds of her forty-five-patient sample, though personal beliefs and practices were more important than institutional forms. When she analysed a smaller number of in-depth interviews the encompassing theme was a search for meaning. 'It makes you think' was a frequent comment.

It is not surprising, therefore, that a number of these patients turned to new discoveries in this area, or reinforced already existing beliefs. St. Christopher's is a Christian as well as a medical foundation but it has no interest in imposing the beliefs of many (though by no means all) of the staff. Rather is it concerned with giving that hospitality that will enable people to find their own answers. Some will want to talk of such matters and I would not have the poems of Brenda Dawson and Sidney Reeman nor the drawings of Miss BH to include if they had not shared with me what they were writing at the time. But some of the patients who were with us for many weeks have either kept their silence on this matter or told us that they definitely did not share our approach. Like Paula and her horny little red devil, they felt quite free and accepted in their attitudes. Ted kept his gently agnostic approach, unpressured to the end.

The same is true for the staff of the Hospice. From the beginning we knew we were to be a community of the unlike, with all members making their own particular and individual contributions. The authors of the staff entries are as varied as the patients, giving of themselves in a spirit of freedom. What we all have in common is a desire to listen.

Listening includes awareness of the whole family. Joan's children felt welcomed and included so that after her death they wanted to return to meet the staff again. Some groups need the intensive work described by Barbara McNulty (the first Hospice Home Care Nurse) and several families have met members of the ward team as they gradually faced their own needs. Others, like Tony's wife, slip quietly into the team and continue as much as they can manage of the caring they carried out at home until it became too much. Mrs Barton's family only needed the Hospice Home Care Nurses to be on call to manage everything themselves in the peace of her daughter's home.

The listening to the search for meaning may mean a costly sharing of deep anguish. As hospice teams have worked so hard and so successfully over the years to relieve physical pain and other symptoms, we may have been tempted to believe that emotional and spiritual pain should be tackled and solved in a similar way. Sometimes unrealistic fears can be explained and eased but a good deal of such suffering has to be lived through. The very pain itself may lead to resolution or a new vision. As Bishop John Taylor puts it, we all remember how it hurts when the circulation returns to a limb that has been numbed or frozen. But it means that we can move again.

Only as members of a team become more experienced and confident do they find it easy to allow or even encourage the expression of the anger and other negative feelings that may reveal this inner pain and the frequent questions 'Why?' We have to learn to listen in a way that will help a person to find the route to the real problem and then to face and handle it. Even to the end the inner self can still stretch and broaden and it is in witnessing this that so many families have found strong comfort for their own journey of bereavement. That journey is poignantly expressed in Mrs Leney's contribution and the strong memories have been illustrated in all the letters I have received from family members of these patients.

Hospice staff may have to stay alongside much anguish or bitterness as people face dependence and parting but the search for meaning and peace can take place more quietly than that. It may be in an unhurried listening to memories from the past as people look back on the story of their lives, reassess what has been important to them and find it falls into place. 'Life has a pattern,' said Mr Brooks as he compared his life as a fireman to his state of being on the 'receiving end'. All this, from the welcome by name at the door of the Hospice, to the time given for seemingly superficial interchange, helps the patients find the place where they can feel, 'I'm me – and it's all right' and lay the story down in quietness. Life is *not* fair, there *are* no easy answers but there is a way to acceptance and peace for the last part of the journey.

Some of these patients have found this in terms of traditional beliefs and from long-held faith; others have reached out at the end, like Paula, in hope; nearly all express love in one way or another.

My own hospice vision is of a God who shares the journey more deeply than we ever can, with all the solidarity of His sacrificial and forgiving love and the strength of His powerlessness; a God who does not prevent the hard things that happen in this free and dangerous world but who instead shares them with us all. As Bishop John Taylor wrote in a Christmas poem, 'I am the undefeated heart of weakness.' I believe that this loving, vulnerable power will outlast all else and holds out an ultimate hope of life through death.

A survey of the hospice units in 1985 showed that just over half had some form of Christian foundation. Those who did not were aware of this dimension and often mentioned staff with a personal commitment. It was also obvious that all had firm rules against any pressure to conform on the part of patients or staff. It was clear how much was given in practical ways with no words either called for or proffered. But it is surely not surprising that some of the stories of this book tell of a spiritual search in a climate that made it safe to reach out in this way. We celebrate a place where 'the new life rising within us' has had an opportunity to grow.

Cicely Saunders, November 1987

1

'He Sends Me People'

Cicely Saunders

When I determined to specialise in the care of the terminally ill I realised a nursing training and an almoner's training were not enough and I must belatedly start again and read Medicine, which I did at St. Thomas's between 1951 and 1957. This was when I met Mrs Barbara Galton, who died in 1961. She was always known as Mrs G in the ward and, indeed, we remained Mrs G and Miss Saunders to the end. I visited her daily for seven years as both student and houseman.

Devic's disease is a rare and incurable form of progressive paralysis with loss of sight.

In July 1954 the chaplain announced at Evensong that there was a blind patient in the wards who would like someone to read to her. I was a fairly idle student in casualty at that time, pining to meet patients again after the arid wastes of first and second MB, so I went to find her. Mrs G was 33 and had been admitted in September 1953 with a sudden onset of paralysis. She made an almost complete recovery and was sent for convalescence in November. Within three weeks she was back again with a severe relapse. Further recoveries and relapses culminated in April in a severe optic neuritis with partial blindness and a complete spastic paraplegia and considerable loss of movement and sensation in her arms. Devic's disease was diagnosed.

From this time until July she had been recovering a little movement and sight and quite a lot of morale. The almoner had recently arranged for two Red Cross visitors to read to her in the afternoons. Her husband and mother were both working but came alternate evenings.

Mrs G was an only child and her mother was a widow, working as manageress at a branch of a chain of restaurants. She and her daughter were very close friends. Her husband had been a policeman, but was then working as a driver. They had been married some years and were very happy together. He looked after their only child, Peter, two and a half, who had asthma and eczema. Neither her husband nor her mother ever missed a visit, always being first through the ward door; they were always truly interested in all her doings and friends in the ward and they kept her in the centre of all their planning of family affairs until the end.

So I met Mrs G. She looked frail but much alive, very pretty and young for her age. It was hard to believe she was nearly-blind, she was so alert and appeared to see all that was going on round her. She had recently begun sitting out of bed. Her legs were rather spastic and had no voluntary movement, and her arms were weak and clumsy with very little sensation. Her medical student had begun reading her *The Kon-Tiki Expedition*, but on the previous day she had been given a lavender bag by a visitor for the London Flower Gift Mission, and she asked me to read the text. It was, 'Jesus said, "I am the light of the world. He that followeth Me shall not walk in darkness but shall have the light of life."' It had been left while she had been asleep and the visitor had not known she was nearly blind. Mrs G said 'I know it doesn't really mean this kind of darkness but for a moment I wondered if it meant I would see again. But can you tell me about it, where it comes from?'

So we began to read the Gospels in J. B. Phillips's translation. The first day she stopped me and said 'Who wrote it? When did it happen? Did it *really* happen?' When I read her the story of The Feeding of the Five Thousand she said 'Wasn't there a supper sometime?' She was very quick and intelligent, but a background completely outside the Church had given no more than that. The story was news from a far country to her for she had never thought of anything outside the ordinary everyday world of people and material things.

Months later she said to me, 'You know, I'm not really sorry this has happened to me. I would never have known all about this, nor how nice people are.' Sometimes I read, usually we discussed, always we gossiped. I could come every day, Sister often let me feed her, more and more often the ward fed me as well. I gave her a *Daily Light* (selected Bible readings for morning and evening). We read and discussed the morning's reading and it became tradition for the nurse who tucked her down at night to read the other. Sometimes they were too busy, sometimes they were not interested, but usually they managed to fit it in. She often asked them, 'Does this help you? Do you believe it?' She said afterwards that she noticed a difference in the many who said 'Yes'. She became really interested and talked to others, her physiotherapy students, the ward sister, her Red Cross visitors.

One day, years afterwards, she was talking to a student about her faith and said, 'Some people read their Bible and find their help there, others can go to church and find it there, but He deals with me differently – He sends me people.' And that is just how He did deal with her. After about nine months she herself began to believe. One day she said to me, talking of Holman Hunt's picture *The Light of the World* which I had described to her, 'I did ask Him to come in a few days ago, but I don't feel any different.' But feeling followed faith. About three weeks later her little boy was desperately ill with measles and pneumonia. She knew because her husband could not hide his anxiety. When she prayed for Peter she found a new confidence and first experienced the feeling of safety, of being looked after, which became more and more real with time.

By now her condition had improved considerably. One day we took her in her wheelchair in an ambulance to see the bluebells at Kew. She could see blue better than any other colour and we all sent her flower postcards and gentians when we could afford them. She tried to learn Braille and Moon but had not enough sensation to manage either. The physiotherapists performed Herculean efforts in getting her upright and walking her, and she learned to make baskets. This she continued to do when she became quite blind and her hands looked quite useless. The visits to the occupational therapy department, the tea parties there and the gossip with the other patients were a great part of her life at one period.

In the summer of 1955 she had two sad blows. Dr Guttmann came to see her from Stoke Mandeville and said she was too disabled for him to help at all. She realised then that she would never go home again either. She shed many bitter tears that evening, but neither then, nor at any time, did she ever say 'Why should this happen to me?' Hers was the Cockney philosophy, 'Oh well, it's just one of those things', but she went on to say, 'It might have happened to my husband – to Peter' – as if to say 'I *can* cope, they mightn't', or 'Someone has to carry this; why not me?'

Not long after this, her first and greatly loved ward sister left. She came often to see Mrs G and take her out in her wheelchair, but there was a difficult patch when she found it hard to adapt herself to the change.

That winter she nearly died of a chest infection. Her intercostal muscles had no power and she could not cough and she got extremely frightened. She spent thirty-six hours in an iron lung, found this rather a joke, and proceeded to recover once again.

Next summer she was moved, without much warning or preparation, to St. Thomas's Country Branch. She had recovered her spirits somewhat by the time she made the journey by ambulance, with a large bunch of the most highly scented flowers that Moyses Stevens could produce on her lap. She tried to settle down but missed her family dreadfully. I was taking part 1 of finals by then, and she made all the nurses promise not to tell me how homesick she was in case I should be worried. We visited when we could and finally

agitated in sympathetic quarters. In September she was transferred back to London, to the Royal Waterloo Hospital (part
of St. Thomas's). She was really at home from the moment
she arrived and here she stayed with the same ward sister till
she died over four years later.

The doctors were slow at considering plans for her transfer
because they had hopes of recovery for a long time and because
they all had such a regard for her. Nor did any of them fully
realise at first how difficult it is to find anywhere suitable for
these patients. At this time we had hopes of a fairly early
vacancy in a small home in Bromley, but neither this vacancy
nor one at the Royal Hospital and Home for Incurables,
Putney, came up until the consultant who had promised to
take her temporarily had, in his turn, fallen under her spell.
Both were cancelled, but indeed hers was a teaching bed used
to very good purpose.

At the Royal Waterloo Hospital she was at last allowed to
have an indwelling catheter and was able to go home to their
flat near by, not only for afternoons, as before, but also for
the occasional weekend. She learned to work her Talking
Book and 'read' quite widely. Her hair was permed and set.
Regularly until her hands became very misshapen we used to
paint her nails, and her husband was the expert at this. She
spent much of the day up in her chair, and somehow she
managed to feed herself.

During the years she had relapses, but with a quite indomitable spirit she pulled up each time. Gradually colours, shapes,
and finally light, left her. Her hands got weaker, her left hand
curled up and her right elbow stiffened. Her legs, strapped
down by day, and addressed firmly by her as if they were
some other ego, always longing to jerk and pull her down the
bed or spoil the comfortable position the nurses had just
achieved, became uncontrollable and caused abdominal pain
if they were not allowed to flex. Intrathecal phenol helped
considerably, but jerks and painful muscle spasms were
part of her life for at least two and a half years. Vertigo
kept her in bed, and finally made all movement and change

of position something to be guarded against. She was a very difficult nursing problem, but the nurses always enjoyed it.

About two years ago she had a very severe relapse. She was unconscious for about three weeks, and confused and unhappy for many weeks afterwards. During this time she finally lost all her positional sense and all sensation below her neck except deep pain. Her only links with the material world were hearing, taste and smell. When this episode was over she was completely her old self once more, but she had no recollection of any unhappiness. Those weeks which had been so hard for her husband and the rest of us were completely lost to her and she settled down to a happy and social routine once again.

Always I remember her laughter. She had a delicious sense of the ridiculous, and especially of the ridiculousness of her own crippled body. She neither pitied it nor hated it; there it was and like everything else in life could be laughed at. From behind the curtains came muffled giggles from the nurses, from the bathroom came quite uncontrollable laughter. It was so hard to remember she was blind. She always looked towards the things she wanted us to see, always knew where they were. She gave us the distinct impression of knowing what we all looked like, right up to the end, when she had seen nothing for so long.

There were bad days. Upsets in routine were increasingly hard for her to cope with as she became really ill. She hated Sister going on holiday or a change of nurses, although the people she liked were always legion. Some patients and many nurses remained her friends for years and she always went on making new ones. Physios and medical students came back again and again to see her. She loved hearing about anything we had done. Any activity or experience was a matter of interest to her, never of envy. She was the best clearing house of gossip in the hospital and delighted in that fact.

The chaplain became one of her many close friends. She did

not ask to be confirmed until a long time after she came to believe, but no one hurried her. She was still up in a chair at that time and she was wheeled to the near-by church. The Bishop came for her alone. A large group of students and nurses came and sang for her and included her favourite, 'Crimond'. One of the small choirboys was so impressed that he went straight home to tell his mother, who was confirmed with two of her friends a few months later.

Mrs G had her own invention of which she was most proud, a face-scratcher. One night she was suffering miseries from an itching nose and could only flex her right arm to about 90 degrees. She tried to think of 'the longest thing in the cubicle' and decided it would be a rolled-up newspaper. Next day her mother bound one to her hand with a handkerchief, she moved her arm vaguely till it hit her face, and could scratch! The final version was a roll of cardboard with a handkerchief tucked in the top, and a further triumph was a spout attached to it and a polythene tube into a jug of water. This was independence indeed and she used to drink six jugfuls a day. Using her arm improved the muscles again and she could reach her face in time. But her hand was useless – 'Silly thing, it just flops about' – and the scratcher remained.

The spirit is more than the body which contains it. Again and again during the last weeks she seemed to compel her mind to come back to reality, or, if she were deluded, to show her own self in the way she reacted to a delusion. Her unconquerable will refused to give up her frail hold on life. About three weeks before she died she whispered to me 'I could have gone last weekend, but I hung on.' But she had learned the trust which I believe gave her quietness at the end. She had talked about prayer to me a few weeks before and said, with her own matter-of-fact simplicity, 'What you pray for you usually get, if it's necessary and if He thinks you ought to have it.' The uncanny organisation of her visitors was one answer. She was so dependent on them when she could no longer manage her Talking Book and they never failed to come just when they were wanted. We did not arrange for the times her mother could not come. It was never necessary.

Mr G was nearly as much of an institution in the ward as his wife and they both made her cubicle its social centre. At one time Mrs G was very sad for him and tried to encourage him to go out elsewhere and not to come so faithfully, but he fitted his life into the cramped lines of the pattern her illness imposed and they continued to love and to enjoy each other deeply. When she became really ill her mother gave up work to sit with her for part of each day. Her firm insisted on paying her full wages for a year until she reached retiring age, in spite of her many attempts to stop them. There was something about Mrs G that brought out the best in almost anyone who had anything to do with her.

Peter has had a somewhat chequered medical history and still goes to a school for the physically handicapped. His father and grandmother are his stability but he has had a real feeling for his mother. She has been someone to visit in hospital, however, not someone who is missing at home. He was affectionate enough towards her to comfort her longing in part, but not enough to be hurt himself. It was the hardest battle she had to fight, but finally she learned, as she put it, 'to pull a curtain down', when she would only make herself uselessly unhappy by thinking of him. But she was not unmindful of the cost to her family – 'I'm being looked after here. It's my mother and my husband . . . They've got to think of the future and keep coming up every day.'

During the last few weeks she was often confused mentally and sometimes she thought we were deceiving her or denying her something. Those of us who loved her found this hard to bear but the sharpness of the pain was only a measure of our long confidence in her faithfulness. It was so utterly unlike the loyalty we had come to rely upon implicitly, for where she loved, she loved without a question.

She died the night her ward sister left for an administrative post after much heart-searching. Neither had to spend one day in the ward without the other. She knew Sister was leaving, as always she sensed it before anything was said, and tackled her directly. There were floods of tears and the old fear of being sent away came out once more. Matron came up to help comfort her and finally did two very practical things: she ordered Mrs G's favourite lunch from the kitchen, and she sent for me. When I arrived Mrs G said, 'Don't worry, I'll dry up sometime . . .' Then later – 'I ate those chips; it was a huge plateful and I said to my mother "I'll eat them if I burst." Now I'll talk about it, but I've told Matron to ask all the nurses not to mention it unless I ask them. I'll only start myself off again.'

And, as it happened, she never had to say goodbye to Sister or to any of us. Mrs G was celebrating Christmas with half a glass of sherry and giggling over it, though she slept through most of Christmas and Boxing Day and woke only fitfully the next two days. Her husband came as usual the last evening. The chaplain, as so often over the years, called in to see them both but she was gradually slipping into deep unconsciousness. During that night she died.

I have a photograph of Mrs G taken in her early twenties. The wide joyous smile in it was just the same when she died. She had become great and her influence had spread to hundreds of people directly or indirectly, but the clear simplicity of her love and interest and enjoyment was unclouded.

It is really impossible to show how much we have all learned through her; I can only try to underline the things that brought her through and made her so triumphant.

First of all, people: her husband and her mother, who never failed her; the two ward sisters who found in her one of their greatest friends; the endless succession of nurses who enjoyed her company and learned to help her complete physical dependence and to respect her great independence of mind and spirit; the doctors who kept her in St. Thomas's for over seven years; and the friends who met her in so many different ways but who all loved her and kept on coming.

Above all it was her own spirit and determination, which

were there from the beginning, and her great but simple faith in God, which grew over the years. She fought a very good fight, and she found and kept the faith.

2

Aunt Winnie and Aunt Mabel

Helen Willans

Helen Willans was Warden of the Drapers' Wing which was established in 1967 as a haven for the frail and the elderly with a particular concern for our own future dependants. She went on to be the Matron of St. Christopher's from 1971-83.

After we had read several of her letters, Mrs Walters was nicknamed 'The Importunate Widow'. She was writing to enquire about the wing for elderly residents being built as part of St. Christopher's Hospice. Before long her enquiries became demands – to be one of the first residents. At this stage it seemed fair to meet her: to be won over by her conviction, arrived at after much prayer, that the Drapers' Wing would be the right future home for her, and she would be right as one of its residents.

In June 1967 Mrs Walters sold up her home in Beckenham and became one of the first four residents. She brought with her the pioneering spirit that had enabled her, as a trained nurse, to serve as Matron of a hospital ship in World War I. If one word could sum up her character it would be 'indomitable'. Life was lived fully, independently and uniquely in her new, small home. She was soon thought of affectionately as 'Aunt Winnie'.

Mrs Walters had known many sorrows, including the death of her greatly loved only son, and of a step-son, both under the age of 21, in World War II; but she was not a woman to look back. In looking forward her great hope was that she might be joined in Drapers' Wing by her elder sister, Miss Mabel Attenborough. Within three years this was possible, and Aunt Mabel moved into a room almost directly under Aunt Winnie.

In appearance and experience the two sisters were very different, yet shared many characteristics. Both were profoundly deaf and had similar, deep voices; Aunt Mabel had very limited sight. Aunt Winnie's life-style included weekly bridge parties for friends from Beckenham, innumerable cigarettes and an ever-open balcony door – which, coupled with disdain for central heating, made visiting her in winter most uncomfortable. Aunt Mabel relished the quiet of her room, welcoming the care and comfort she received and continuing a ministry of prayer and Bible study, aided by a powerful magnifying glass. Once or twice every week Aunt Winnie joined Aunt Mabel for tea and cakes and 'a little game of patience'. This ritual gave both satisfaction and was accompanied by wildly whistling hearing aids.

As children, the sisters had been brought up as Baptists, and both had developed a vital, personal faith. After sixty years teaching Sunday School and worshipping at Walworth Road Baptist Church, Aunt Mabel attended a Congregational church. At the Hospice she valued receiving Communion in her room, as she could neither see nor hear what was going on in Chapel. Aunt Winnie had become an Anglican in later life and was a regular attender at the Hospice Chapel.

Inevitably, and at first imperceptibly, both the aunts became less active. Aunt Winnie continued to do her own shopping in Penge, regardless of blue extremities and an ever-worsening cough. Her hope and prayer now was that she would outlive Aunt Mabel. For her part, Aunt Mabel graciously accepted increasing assistance and showed little sign of anxiety.

In 1971, after a short period endeavouring to cope with quickly increasing frailty, Aunt Winnie agreed she needed nursing care. Four days later she died peacefully in a side room of a Hospice ward, aged 91. Aunt Mabel grieved quietly and undoubtedly missed her sister deeply. She was comforted by her well-tried faith and the certainty that she would follow before too long. In 1974, now almost completely blind and deaf and following a fall, Aunt Mabel moved to Princess Alexandra Ward where she allowed the staff to give her every care until she also died, four months later. She was 97.

Perhaps the most outstanding quality of character shared by these sisters was courage, albeit shown in very different ways. Aunt Mabel's character and personality were dominated by patience, gentleness and humour, with an inner core of steel-like strength. Aunt Winnie's strength was visible, as were her humour and common sense: it was her inner core that was so very gentle.

3

A Will to Live

Sheila Gamsu

Tony was at St. Christopher's between 1968 and 1970. Staff Nurse Sheila Gamsu's account of his time here is quoted from one of the chapters I contributed to 'On Dying Well: an Anglican contribution to the debate on euthanasia', published by the Church Information Office, London, in 1975.

Tony was admitted to a hospice suffering from motor neurone disease, a neurological illness at present incurable, which affects the muscles progressively but has no effect on sensation or mental alertness. During a two-and-a-half-months' stay he gained confidence in his now limited capacity, and his wife was able to take on part-time work. After trial weekends he returned home indefinitely on the understanding that he would be readmitted immediately should the need arise. Seven and a half months later they both decided that they could manage no longer. This time together had been good but, as his wife said, 'What we have together now is so splendid that I would hate to jeopardise it by becoming too tired to cope – and we do get frightened sometimes.' On readmission he could still do a little for himself and enjoyed reading and music. Over the course of two years he became progressively dependent on others and more and more easily fatigued. Gradually his tape-recorder, his wheelchair outings and even long conversations became too much for him. He lost his voice, but his wife and several members of staff learned to lipread what he said, and he waited with endless patience while they persevered.

As Tony became aware that he was not going to recover from his illness, he began to talk about dying; he was not afraid of death, but of *how* he would die. As swallowing became more of an effort, so his fear of choking to death increased. He spoke of euthanasia and asked, 'Why should I go on living in this way?' While we could sympathise with these feelings and certainly did not want Tony to suffer any more, at the same time the thought of euthanasia was impossible for any of us to contemplate. *Who would give the fatal injection?* When would we know that the time had really come? Tony, well aware of *our* feelings on the subject, could appreciate the difficulties. He was ambivalent about this desire, for just as frequent were his requests that anyone suffering from a cold or sore throat should not go too near him. He would say, 'I could not throw off a cold; it might prove fatal!' We also learned that he had asked his wife while he was still at home to give him an overdose of sleeping pills at a time when he could no longer reach out for them for himself. She could not bring herself to do this. They discussed it and agreed that, while they could perhaps take an overdose for themselves, neither of them could contemplate giving one to the other.

Tony was deeply involved in all that was going on around him. Even though he was unable to talk so that they could hear him, other patients included him in their conversations. In the next bed was a young man with multiple sclerosis who was also blind. Although the two could communicate only through others, a close friendship developed between them. In spite of all his physical disabilities and many frustrations, Tony was still able to be concerned about others and talk with wit and directness. He would give a warm smile to any who spoke with him, especially when they finally battled through to understand what he was conveying to them.

Throughout his long illness Tony's wife visited him regularly and frequently. She would sit close to him, chatting, reading, feeding him; and then before leaving she would settle him down comfortably for the night in a deft and capable way which none of the nurses could match; she knew just how he liked to be. From what had been a rather unstable marriage before Tony's illness there grew an unusually close and loving relationship. This gave them strength and confidence to go on together until Tony died peacefully in his sleep. He had by then become confident that he would not be allowed to choke, and when he had a massive pulmonary embolus he slipped easily into unconsciousness and died in a few hours.

Tony's ambivalent thoughts about euthanasia are typical. One moment a patient may express a definite wish for it; the next make some comment (as he often did) which shows that his desire to avoid death and to go on living is still strong. Some change their opinions completely. Another young man, also with motor neurone disease, was admitted to the bed opposite Tony. On one occasion he said to the night sister, 'If I ever got like that chap I'd want to do something to myself.' In fact, when he finally reached almost exactly the same condition in his turn, he found that his feelings had changed and that the experience from inside was not what it appeared to the onlooker. To one of the doctors he said, 'I can't see round the next bend, but I know it will be all right.' He found, as he said, that what he had experienced and what he had seen in others was a 'bringing-together illness. In this kind of life the complexities fall away; what is left is what matters.'

4

The Dragon and the Flowers

Cicely Saunders

Miss BH was a school teacher, head of a large modern languages department, who spent five weeks in St. Christopher's before her death in April 1970. Glad of the peace of a single room, she used her time in talking with good friends and in writing and illustrating a book for children. This was never published but she allowed me to make slides of a few of the illustrations.

Her story began with a child setting out on a journey of search with two companions, a grey cat and a brown bird. The child sports a jaunty feather in its cap. All three stride out confidently. The sun is shining through the trees and the ground is covered in flowers. Before reaching the end of their journey the three friends have to cross a particularly busy road while a typically British bobby holds up the traffic in his shirt-sleeves.

As Miss BH was completing this picture I happened to be taking a Swedish psychiatrist round St. Christopher's and, with her permission, we had a private view. He interpreted the scene as a full stop and said, 'I don't think she'll do another drawing. That policeman is holding her up.' He was wrong.

The book completed, Miss BH went on drawing lively pictures of children. One, of two little girls dancing towards a Christmas tree, became the Hospice's Christmas card the following year.

This picture was completed a few days before Miss BH died and we discussed its meaning together. The dragon represented her illness and she was the child. Although the dragon is so much bigger than she is, and although it is eating her flowers, yet that child is not afraid. She left the drawing for me to use as I liked.

5

A Holding Role

Barbara McNulty

Together with Dr Mary Baines, Sister Barbara McNulty set up St. Christopher's Home Care Service in 1969. It was funded initially through a research and development grant from the then Ministry of Health for which I originally applied in 1966. She worked as one of our original Ward Sisters from 1967 to 1969 and finally retired in 1976.

John was 48, he was tall, slim and prematurely grey, a good-looking and successful engineer. He was a Scot, friendly, intelligent, likeable, obstinate and independent. He faced life with a certain cynicism, calling himself an agnostic with shades of atheism. He was married with two children, a son of 16 (Peter) and a daughter of 18 (Pam). The marriage was a good one with considerable love and understanding, the children were clever and both had done well at school. His wife, Jane, was friendly, outgoing and easygoing, busy and active with many outside interests.

In 1966 John had investigations for persistent toothache which revealed a malignant tumour of his upper jaw; he underwent extensive facial surgery and it was hoped that all would be well. A few months later, however, he had a recurrence of the tumour and further surgery. Following this he remained fairly well for several years until his hopes were dashed by a further growth of the tumour requiring still more surgery.

The strain of five years of illness was beginning to tell on the family when in March 1971, John and Jane were referred to St. Christopher's by their general practitioner for 'moral support'. This, my first contact with the family, happened just ten days before John was due to have his left eye removed, the fourth operation to his face. The family was stunned by the shock and unable to do anything but close ranks and try not to think of the implications.

On my first visit to the home my impression was of a tight-knit, closed family circle. Jane was protective and anxious to show that she could cope. They presented a picture of a united couple, well in control of the situation and confident of a cure. They were anxious for me to understand that John could not be too bad as he had been playing golf a week before. When his wife went out of the room John admitted that he had constant pain and that he felt depressed and anxious about the future. John was a brave man, and he did not share his anxieties easily, but it seemed to me that he was beginning to feel very frightened and had no one in whom he could confide. I was a stranger and I was uninvolved in his illness, so he could lower his defences slightly and tell me something of how he felt. This first confidence was important for it laid the foundation for our relationship.

I did not see John again until five weeks later when he had had further extensive surgery to his face. During his time in hospital his wife kept touch with me by telephone to let me know how he was getting on. These telephone conversations proved to be important, for they became the ground for my relationship with her. She also needed a confidant with whom to share her anxieties, and it was she who asked me to visit when John came out of hospital.

They still presented a united and optimistic front, but this time I was included, and they shared with me some of the difficulties they were experiencing in dealing with his wound and I was able to make practical suggestions. It was almost as though we could talk about *the* wound or *the* discharge as though they were entities separate from John himself, and therefore safe to talk about.

During the next few weeks of finding ways of overcoming John's physical pain we got to know one another better. He was no longer depressed and his fears receded. He hoped and he tried to believe that he was now cured.

He was constantly asking for some reassurance on this, but never waited for a reply, keeping me at a distance. His wife, however, always managed to get me alone before I left the house. She went over and over what was being done, what had been done, what the surgeon had told John, and what she herself had been told, which was much less optimistic. She described every symptom and every tiny variation of symptom and wanted to know its meaning and significance. She was frightened and anxious. I would sometimes sit for as much as an hour saying nothing while she poured out her grief and her worry.

John began to improve a little. He had an excellent prosthesis in his mouth and a very convincing false eye. As his pain came under control he was able to play golf and garden a little. His mood varied from confident elation to withdrawn depression. He did not tolerate drugs well, and efforts to get him to take anti-depressants had to be abandoned. He hated the idea of being dependent on drugs of any kind, and resented the analgesics which he had to have. He would sometimes demonstrate his independence by varying the times at which he took his pills and occasionally he would decrease the dose. Although these efforts were always disastrous from the point of view of the control of his symptoms, they were important to John in that they gave him a feeling of being in charge of the situation, of being his own master. I tried to support him in these efforts, though he often felt guilty afterwards and his wife felt reproachful of him.

The relationship between them was becoming less open than it had been. Jane knew the truth about the future and felt isolated with her knowledge. John suspected the truth but could not voice it. There were sharp quarrels from time to time which left both of them feeling sad and bewildered. My role was a holding one, supporting John while he came to terms with his fears about the future, and reassuring Jane that this phase of angry resentment would pass.

They both began to feel that it might help to get away for a holiday, and a 3-4 week stay in a cottage was planned. Jane asked for my home phone number and said she would report in regularly and would feel safer if she knew she could talk to me. The day before they were due to go I had a frantic phone call to say that Pam, the 18-year-old daughter, had taken an overdose and was unconscious.

Pam was a shy, highly strung girl who adored her father. His illness had distressed her deeply and his disfigurement was past enduring. She had refused to talk about his illness and tried to keep away from the house as much as possible. I had met her once, and had heard something of her problems from her mother. I think now that I should have tried harder to get to see her, but at the time I had felt that I could not push too much.

John was beside himself with anger which masked a fear. He kept saying that he could not understand why she should do such a thing. I suggested that perhaps it was because of her anxiety about him, but he rejected this at once. A week later Pam came out of hospital and the whole family went off to the cottage.

I had two cheerful postcards saying that John had been gardening, had built a stone wall and done some maintenance work in the cottage. They had been away four weeks when in early September John had a sudden set-back and they returned home. I saw him at once and made a note that 'he seems to be very anxious under a calm exterior'. He was having difficulty in speaking and was unable to swallow anything but liquids, nevertheless he was still trying to keep up the pretence that this was nothing serious, and he would not discuss it.

Jane was frantic with worry, and kept me a long time telling me how well he had been during the holiday, as though trying to excuse herself for some oversight or lack of care, for which she felt guilty. She asked endless questions . . . what could be the cause of this deterioration and what its significance? What would 'they' do now? There were no easy answers to her questions. I felt that it was important to maintain the stand that I had taken all along with both of them. 'Of course we hope that things will improve, but it doesn't look too good at the moment.' In other words, no facile words of misplaced cheer, yet always keeping the door open to a realistic hope.

Both children had enjoyed the holiday, which in some way had smoothed over the cracks appearing in their lives, by its apparent normality. During the next few days I saw both separately for the first time. Pam did not want to talk about her overdose or her anxieties about her father, but I felt that I could not leave it at that. I asked her straight out whether she thought she might do it again and she said she would not. I said I understood how she must feel and added that I should be grateful for any help she could give me in making things easy for him. She nodded but said nothing.

Peter had failed his O-levels in the summer and he admitted that his father's illness had made it difficult for him to concentrate. He asked questions about the progress of the cancer and wanted explanations about the operations, which I gave briefly. From being something of a tearaway he had become very responsible about the house and very concerned about his mother's distress. I did not feel that his involvement in household affairs was a healthy thing and finally decided to say that I thought his job was to do well in his exams and not to get too stuck in household chores. Jane co-operated in this and encouraged him to go out and play football and see his friends.

John was becoming much less well. I noted that he was retiring into himself and cutting himself off from people. Speech was difficult and often I just sat beside him talking quietly, occasionally he wrote on his scribble pad. I spent a lot of time with Jane listening to a minute-by-minute account of the previous twenty-four hours, and I saw the children about once a week, not in formal pre-arranged meetings, but just by chance if they happened to be in when I called.

On October 5th I wrote 'The situation is deteriorating, he sleeps a lot and weeps sometimes. His wife is still sharing the double bed and he conveys his feelings to her by holding her hand lovingly. She feels that this is as much as he can do, or she expect, in the way of communication. He has bouts of depression when he gazes into a mirror and shakes his head. He speaks very little.' It was at this point that we discussed the failure of the recent operation to achieve its goal, and the fact that things were not going as well as he had hoped. He simply nodded his head. He confirmed that he wanted to remain at home and accepted a mild sedation to alleviate anxiety. He stated that he was not afraid. This whole conversation implied his understanding of his true situation, it was a turning-point in his illness. Until then he had been hoping for a cure and fighting against the truth. He had maintained an exterior of independence with episodes of furious anger directed against his wife and family. Now his mood changed: he was less depressed but often irritable and suspicious of any drug changes. He became mildly paranoid, believing that his wife and I were trying to poison him, began to refuse his drugs and became difficult to handle. I noted that 'this aspect of his character had always been there, but well concealed and controlled'.

Early in November his GP read him the riot act about his lack of co-operation. John was outraged and upset; he wept when he told me about it, but I think it was a well-timed reminder of reality which served to move him into the next phase of his coming to terms with death. Not long after, John wrote on his scribble pad 'I know the doctors can't do any more for me, but don't you know anyone who can?' 'Who?' I asked. 'A faith healer.' I promised to find him one.

Through a series of coincidences I was able to go back a few days later with Father Michael, a man who was to change John's and Jane's lives. He was not a faith healer in the commonly accepted meaning of the term, but he was a man of faith; he visited them once or twice a week for the next seven weeks and became a loved and valued friend.

John was much calmer and more at peace; he seemed to accept his deterioration completely, and though he was weak and weary he was mentally alert and cheerful. Jane remained very anxious and developed 'premonitions' that he was about to die at any minute. She wanted to talk about his death, what would it be like, what should she do, who should she call, and so on. We made detailed plans for every eventuality and she had permission to phone me at any time.

Meanwhile John saw his solicitor and put his affairs in order. He went about it in a matter-of-fact sort of way and there were no more tears or fits of anger. Jane moved out of their bedroom as she was sleeping badly and beginning to show signs of strain. She felt guilty about it, and needed much reassurance that she was managing extremely well. The children moved about the house silently, awkwardly, miserably. I saw them whenever they wanted to talk. They could not bear to see their father and felt unable to reach their mother, and for a while I was the link between them all.

By the end of November John was becoming difficult again: one day he would be rational and lucid, the next rambling, questioning, searching. The strain on the family was becoming unbearable and was seriously affecting Jane and the children. John needed only a little persuasion to accept admission to the Hospice; he wept a little and then agreed.

During the remaining thirty-six days of his life a great deal happened to John. His relationship with his wife returned to the close loving thing it had been before his illness. Jane, once the full responsibility of caring for him had been taken off her shoulders, was able to relax and sit with him for much of the day, doing little things for him and reading to him. The children came in once or twice, but only briefly and not very happily. I continued to see them from time to time.

John had his good days and his bad days. Sometimes he would gaze morbidly at his mutilated face in the mirror for hours on end, or he would refuse to do whatever he was asked and would wither whoever was there with a baleful glance. On other days he, who had been so proudly independent, would allow Jane to do things for him which he had never allowed before, and would be grateful. It seemed to me that he was almost overwhelmed by the appalling horror of his illness, yet now his basic character reappeared. In spite of enforced dependence on others he was in command. He took his drugs when he decided to and not when the nurses gave them to him. He did what he wanted to, when he wanted to, and it was important that we let him do so.

When he could hardly write, he sent a note to all the nurses apologising for all the trouble he gave them, and thanking them for their care.

He asserted his dignity as an individual and it was our role to confirm his individuality and his integrity.

Father Michael visited weekly and the relationship between him and John continued well. Something was happening to John which manifested itself by his coming back into the church and by him and Jane taking Communion together on Christmas Day.

On the morning of January 1st, 1971 John woke early, restless and irritable. He sent for his wife and he sent for me. We came and sat on either side of his bed talking quietly, not sure whether he could hear us or not. About mid morning he opened his one eye and looked at us. Putting his hands together in an attitude of prayer he turned to me and nodded his head imperiously. There was no mistaking the command, but I was unsure how to comply. My efforts at the Twenty-third Psalm were cut short peremptorily, he would have none of it. I looked at him and a little uncertainly began reciting the commendatory prayers for the dying. 'Lord into thy hands I commend my spirit, and all those whom I love.' John was satisfied. He gave a little wave of his hand first to his wife and then to me and went to sleep. He never regained consciousness, yet when Father Michael came in late that evening and prayed with him John knew he was there and responded with the lightest pressure of his hand, no other movement. He died at four minutes past midnight.

I have told this story, this true story, because it illustrates so well the counselling role of every one of the people involved.

The doctor who could deal effectively and sympathetically with the physical symptoms and knew how to set the boundaries to John's behaviour with directness and firmness. The chaplain who entered unhesitatingly into a committed relationship, giving profoundly of himself. The nurses who allowed John to be himself, to find himself, by containing his anger and grief in a loving, caring way.

For myself, it was my work with this family which awakened me to the possibilities of therapy with the dying and their families and kindled my interest in counselling. I see my own role in this case as having been one of caring continuity. I provided a bridge between the members of the family when communications broke down, a refuge and support to each one, my relationship to each being one of mutual trust and respect, and I provided a link with the other professionals involved. The key to all our roles was I think 'commitment' with a willingness to enter unjudgmentally into the drama – the tragedy which was being played.

The points that this case history illustrates so comprehensively will not all be present in every dying situation, but all will be met with at some time.

The patient's slow, developing realisation of his incurable condition was accompanied at first by disbelief that it could really be happening to him. Then there was a kind of hope that perhaps if he underwent the surgery and the treatment suggested all might be well, then anger and resentment that treatment had not succeeded, and finally some sort of resolution which came about through his facing the reality of what was happening and accepting that he was going to die.

These stages were not lived through in isolation because John's family were closely involved and drawn into every stage. What often becomes unbearable for the family and can contaminate the whole dying process are the quarrels and recriminations, the bitterness and the guilt which distance people from one another at a time when they most need to come together.

In this instance, the wife needed reassurance that she was

managing extremely well and that the harsh unhappy phases were only phases and would pass.

The children had to be considered for their individual and very different needs, and the patient himself needed a sense of security based on trust and truth in an atmosphere in which he could be himself and find his own solution. Those of us who were involved in caring for this family also needed encouragement in the difficult times, and we provided one another with support at regular meetings.

I followed up this family for about eight months. On the whole their grief followed a normal course. Loneliness, isolation and guilt were very much part of Jane's recovery. Peter up to a point took over his father's role, but Jane was aware of this and tried to help him to develop. Pam perhaps was the most disturbed, but slowly began to take up a normal life.

Through all this 'unjust', 'undeserved' and unlooked for suffering, every one of the dramatis personae was changed and in some way matured and grew. Not least, the patient himself was transformed, and that surely is what life and death is all about.

6

Paula

Cicely Saunders

We continually meet hope among people with mortal or long-term illness – hope that springs out of reality and from facing and tackling a situation, however bleak it may be.

I remember Paula, who was blonde and beautiful, still young but in 1972 already bedridden with advanced disease. She was facing the certain outcome like the tough and realistic person she was. She had always lived her life day by day – it had been that sort of life – and she still did so without much thought of anything beyond the world of her immediate surroundings and with a wry self-centredness. When she said, 'I try not to moan,' she added, 'I just don't want people to remember me as a nasty person!' We remember her all right. And all the clutter she accumulated round her bed, and the horny little red devil she had placed on the wall niche where a small cross had been . . . looking at us sideways to see if we had noticed and taken the point.

All the time she was with us she used to join in our teaching rounds. We would bring groups of students to her room (with her permission) and, well used to entertaining, she used to show them that what really mattered was what someone was like – not how ill they might be.

Her appearance mattered a lot to her and she was always immaculate, even on the days when things nearly got on top of her. She was demanding of our time and interest but took an equal interest in our doings in her turn, an entertainer and a good friend to the end. She was concerned with the general doings of the Hospice (though not too much with the other patients) and we used to discuss all sorts of things with her.

On her last night I was sitting in her room for an evening gossip when she suddenly said, 'All I hope is that I can sit in that chair and watch the nurses make this bed . . . but I wonder . . .' During the night she became much worse; but first she had a long talk with the Night Sister, asking her what she believed was the meaning of life and if there was anything beyond it. At the end Paula said, 'I can't say I believe like that . . . would it be all right if I just said that I hoped?' With that she took off her false eyelashes and, asking Sister to put them away, said 'I won't need them any more . . .' Within a day she had died, keeping us all at her beck and call to the end.

Hope means being vulnerable and ready to take off masks and pretence, ready to reach out trustfully without even knowing what is the truth for which you long. It also means being able, as Night Sister was, to speak simply of the truth as you see it. Her hope, which was in Jesus Christ, met Paula's longing and helped her to make the simple gesture of being just herself and to reach out into the darkness of death and not be afraid.

Hope for Paula at the end of her short life meant being vulnerable and open and ready to take the next step, trusting in the unknown, Good News from a far country . . .

7

Death of a Daughter

Norah Leney

Mrs Leney's daughter, Susan, was at St. Christopher's from July 1972 to May 1974. Her mother's poems of mourning and reconciliation, *In a Lifetime*, were published in 1975.

The Consultant gave me the prognosis. 'She could live six months, it could be longer.' The condition was inoperable.

Susan was only eighteen years old. Dear God – give me health and strength to see her through whatever lies ahead. In retrospect I know a mumps virus caused her death, but as we came through the years before the investigation and observation all was a mystery. She grew ten inches in one year, outgrowing her co-ordination. Her school work deteriorated and she became puzzled by her inability to do things she had accomplished easily before.

Following an examination when she was fifteen, an 'air-bubble X-ray' was taken: the condition of the cerebellum was such that the X-ray seemed impossible to read.

No more schooling for Susan, a light job, with visits to the neurologist every two months.

Her eighteenth birthday came in June 1969. She had a full-time light job, and she was coping. But in August she became very ill with a high temperature, was conscious but not lucid. The neurologist recommended readmission to hospital where her condition worsened. Nothing could be done but wait. Suddenly her temperature dropped and tests could be made.

Quite by chance a local histologist tested the blood samples for antibodies and mumps antibodies were found. A brain biopsy was performed and the inoperable condition was discovered.

The mumps virus had destroyed an enzyme, upsetting the metabolism, fatty deposits in the blood were not being broken down but were gathering in the brain. The mumps virus multiplied, breaking down the cells in the cerebellum, thus the degeneration progressed. The neurologist put it in lay terms for me explaining that as an engine with too heavy an oil would grind to a halt, so would Sùsan.

She came home, her faith supporting her. The local rector brought a Christian healer until she said, 'He's wasting time.' And I knew she knew.

I prayed all the time that someone somewhere had got it wrong, but as her co-ordination deteriorated I knew no mistake had been made. At times she expressed anger, frustrated by her clumsiness, then apologised.

Her intellect was impaired only in that her present memory went. She forgot her inability to walk and would get up to cross the room, crash to the floor, bringing furniture down on top of her, apologising while I sorted it out, helped her up, shaken and bruised. She forgot her accidents and clumsiness, which, had she remembered, would have destroyed her.

The six months passed.

Supported by Susan's strong faith my own grew, the learning experience became a challenge to find more ways to help her retain her independence and dignity.

The wheelchair that had been offered had to be collected and brought into use. We named it 'Genevieve' and I was able to take her out for 'rides' in our immediate neighbourhood: she enjoyed that spring in the lanes and fields around us.

After three years, managing at home became increasingly difficult and the next decision had to be made.

In July 1972 Susan was admitted to St. Christopher's Hospice, where with loving care from a dedicated staff and symptom control for the involuntary movement, Susan blossomed.

That first Christmas at St. Christopher's four theological students came on placement to assist the Chaplain and gain experience working alongside the Hospice staff.

It soon became obvious that one of the students was very important to Susan and he chose to spend a lot of time with her. From seeking her out he started taking her out in her wheelchair. She glowed with happiness: she loved him and he loved her.

So her life was further enriched.

I wondered, was it compassion he felt?

When he left St. Christopher's he wrote to her frequently. The days his letters, or cards, arrived were very special days which the nurses were so happy to share with her. Communication was now more difficult, her speech slow, but from time to time she made profound statements which shook us all.

Her faith and courage inspired others and she made many friends.

Only when it became known that her days were now numbered and all her friends visited 'just once more' was I really aware of the number of people who had come to know and love her and enjoy her company.

I was overwhelmed when she said 'I'm going to be all right, Mummy, but what about you?'

When a friend wept at the death of a mutual friend Susan said, 'Don't be sad, death is just another adventure.'

Had euthanasia been authorised and the Doctor, knowing the prognosis, had the authority to end her life, all this would have been lost.

The 'could be six months' grew, to every one's amazement to four and a half years, when so much had been shared and enjoyed. In the last weeks of tying up loose ends, going back to discussions left unfinished earlier in her life, times I had felt it necessary to correct her firmly and felt sorry about it, she reassured, saying, 'Don't worry, Mummy, you had to do it then; it doesn't matter now.'

Our love and understanding deepened.

Euthanasia would have prevented all this and robbed me of the memories from which I now draw strength, not only to go on without her but to help others.

Later, at the reception following the ordination of the theological student, his Mother sought me out and said, 'Our son loved your daughter – but he could not bear to stay and watch her die – so he went away.'

She Died

She died –
   so peacefully and beautifully
she moved beyond our reach –
Beyond the gate we'd talked about,
   Into that brilliant light,
To peace and wholeness once again.

But we who stayed behind are quietened
   by her passing
and pause on tip-toe
   Listening for her voice to join
   the Angels who rejoice
As they adore Him –
   Lord of all,
Who in his mercy
   Took her by the hand and led her home.

Grief

Deep sobs –
that start beneath my heart
and hold my body in a grip that hurts.
The lump that swells inside my throat
brings pain that tries to choke.
Then tears course down my cheeks –
I drop my head in my so empty hands
abandoning myself to deep dark grief,

and know that with the passing time
will come relief.
That though the pain may stay
There soon will come a day
When I can say her name and be at peace.

Anguish

'It will do you good' they said –
    and took me off by bus and train
I wondered will I rest again?
    but still we journeyed on –
They didn't hear my 'No'
    I didn't want to go

I followed
    I'd abandoned keeping up,
Bewildered, unable to absorb all that I saw,
    I wanted just to rest awhile
amidst my country-side and think my thoughts away,
    until I feel that I can cope with all that comes my way,
by night or day
    Please let me – .

Exhaustion

Just shallow gentle breaths I breathe
and wonder when will energy return?
    Then suddenly lungs skip a breath and
deep lung-filling gulps of air are needed
    by my body.
Hands slightly tremble as I fight to lift my eyelids
and continue with the day.
My soul feels strangely empty and my scalp
just pricks and creeps as if a million
ants invade my hair –

and then my eyelids droop again
I just abandon all to sleep.

Question

Two souls run parallel
  could it be?
One myself
  The other watching me?
Two souls suffering differently
One aches and weeps
The other takes it philosophically.

Strange feelings in affinity
  one knows that time will heal
the other wants to grieve,
  one carries burdens deep within that rend the heart to
    see
the other too tired to deceive.

So we struggle on
myself and I
I take it on the chin,
  and I just cry.

Today

Today a song-bird sang –
Perched so high on yonder tree
Against a sky of silver grey
Full throated song to fill the air
And lift all care away –
I stayed to listen.

8

Visiting at St. Christopher's

Tricia Rusling

Mrs Rusling's mother-in-law was in St. Christopher's from August 1973 to December 1974. The Hospice no longer has its two six-bed bays which, on the whole, proved less satisfactory than the current arrangement of four-bed bays with an extra bathroom on each ward.

When we first heard that my mother-in-law was being transferred to St. Christopher's, we were delighted that she was going to be so near, but this was tempered with apprehension. Until her transfer she had been in a hospital general ward with all the attendant discomforts imposed by lack of privacy, staff shortages, etc. But knowing that St. Christopher's was now to become her home, we were very apprehensive.

I can honestly say my anxiety was dispelled on my first visit. I can remember vividly, arriving at the Hospice a few hours after Mollie's admission, walking into reception with a child of fifteen months in my arms and being greeted with a very warm smile and a 'Can I help you?' I was not just told where to go, I was shown the lift and somebody else took me up to the ward and showed me where Mollie's bed was, as if she had been there for years. I can't put into words how this made me feel; it was a real home, not just a detached institution. The welcome and good impression created by that initial meeting lasted with us until the end.

There were six beds in Mollie's ward, but at no time did she or her visitors feel any lack of privacy. Edward was fifteen months when Mollie arrived and Nicholas was born six months later, but at no time during our fifteen months of visiting did I feel they were frowned upon. In fact I really feel this is why St. Christopher's succeeds in its objectives because Mollie was able to have her home life brought to her, seeing her grandchildren grow up – through breast-feeding to potty training and play to reading – and this all happened round her bed. I even left Nicholas in his carry-cot to be 'baby-sat' by Mollie. Even though she was unable to move, and the total responsibility was the staff's – emotionally, as a granny, she was overwhelmed and felt she had done her duty!

Children are a terrific therapy and conversation is never at a loss. Clearly when visiting very regularly for such a long period it would have been impossible to 'dump' the children and I know I was only able to visit when I did because I could spontaneously just walk out of our house and go straight to the Hospice with the children. St. Christopher's obviously suffered to some extent as accidents do happen, such as unsuspecting neighbours having their air-beds pumped up and pebbles from the stone garden being liberally distributed around the Pilgrim Room! But we were never made to feel embarrassed by having young children in the ward and, indeed, patients, staff and the children alike used to look forward to the visits.

Weekend outings were always encouraged and the care with which Mollie was made up before we arrived was a tremendous morale booster for her. She was never made to feel that it was an inconvenience. One of her nurses even came in off duty to prepare Mollie for a wedding she was going to. That is just the sort of attention to small details that we were conscious of all the time. Any day out was encouraged and talked about for some days afterwards which made Mollie feel far less hospitalised.

Monday at St. Christopher's is the only non-visiting day. From our point of view it was a real day of rest. We were able to be at home and not feel guilty that we were not visiting. Being honest, we really appreciated it. But when Mollie's brother happened to be over from Holland on a Monday he was welcomed as on any other day, given lunch and allowed to stay as long as he wanted. This was typical of how there were rules and no rules.

Visiting at St. Christopher's has left many genuinely happy memories. Being there enabled Mollie to enjoy the last months of her life as much as she could, and all the people who loved her could not have wished her to be in a more perfect place.

I genuinely missed visiting St. Christopher's after Mollie died, as it had become part of our life. Edward, who is now three, still insists on our driving past and he loved his visits to the Hospice, which to me is one hundred per cent proof of the wonderful place it is.

9

Keeping in Touch

Cicely Saunders

Joan was 29 and her four children aged from 4 to 13 when she first met the St. Christopher's Hospice team in 1973. The hospital which had been treating her cancer had found that in spite of all their efforts it was spreading and becoming very painful and they asked the Hospice to control her pain and help her to live as well as she could for the rest of her life.

At first, good pain control meant that she was mostly at home and she made a brave fight to struggle on, but for her last months in 1975 the Hospice gave her a room to herself where her family could visit as much as they liked. Altogether, she had well over a year in which her pain was tackled and controlled and she felt in charge of all that happened. Her family were in and out and made it home, and gradually Joan and her husband Alan talked through all that was happening and she helped him to plan the life of the family that she knew she would not see grow up. They were all helped by the care and friendship of the girl next door, whom Alan later married happily.

Joan kept alert and cheerful to the end of her life, even though she gradually had to give up walking and finally even sitting out in a chair. Her bedside was a centre of attention for them all.

Alan wrote to the Hospice afterwards, 'Joan accepted what life gave her and the skill and loving care of the Hospice, coupled with her determination, gave her an extra year of life – this chapter of my life has been filled with loving care and kindness which I have never come across in life before.'

For several years the whole family came back visiting

because they felt they wanted to see the Hospice again and we were happy to see them growing up, feeling secure even as they faced the loss of their mother. Now, more than twelve years later, they still write and keep in touch.

10

Declaration of Dependence

Sidney Reeman

Sidney Reeman was a patient in St. Christopher's Hospice from November 1974 to March 1975. During this time he started writing poetry after a long gap.

Sunset over Sydenham

I have witnessed smouldering sunsets
Over Sydenham
With colossal cloud formations
And such miracles of mirages
As to be confronted in SE26
With alpine splendour in superb artistry.
I was sustained by those sunsets
But not by evening star.
The loss fading into insignificance
Because the dayspring from on high
Had visited me; Alfred Lord T.
Asked for one clear call
When he put out to sea.
I am not planning anything maritime,
But I hope that there will be
A smouldering sunset over Sydenham.

SR, December 15th, 1974

Hospice Windows

Daily an unidentified bird
Soars over the tree tops
Seeking rest and finding none.

The signs are confusing,
Especially if the A to Z
Is looked at upside down
Or if a bird thinks itself in Sydenham
And finds a signpost marked Penge.
May Christ be praised that in this dwelling
I find respite.
Not having to flit from twig to twig
The signs are clear for the rest of the journey,
The word of God, the Church, the Sacraments,
Combined with an outgiving of self.
I shall not lose my way.
If I do not throw away the map.

SR, December 27th, 1974

Sweeping the Hours

The second-hand of my watch
Does the circular tour of the hours
Sweeping the days away with almost cat-like stealth,
Scoring the point that time lurks in the shadows
Whilst we play out on the open stage
The drama which we label life.
To be told that the latter is terminal
Is a gracious act of a loving God.
Those hours swept away can be employed
In the sweeping of the soul seven times
And mounting guard against further invasion.
Lord, if I make clean and put my house in order,
Grant that I may not undo the work
By spiritual smugness and petty presumption.
Lord, I believe, please help my unbelief.

SR, January 14th, 1975

In the Midst of Life

Death and I are only nodding acquaintances,
We have not been formally introduced,

But many times I have noticed
The final encounter
Here in this Hospice.
I can truly say
That death has been met with dignity
Who can divine the thoughts
Of a man in close confrontation!
I can only remember
One particular passing
When a man,
With sustained smile,
Pointed out what was for him
Evidently a great light
Who knows what final revelations
Are received in the last hours?
Lord, grant me a star in the East
As well as a smouldering sunset.

SR, January 28th, 1975

Murmurings

Low murmurings from your creation, Lord
Despite the fact that I am full of thy praise.
In your supreme wisdom, Lord,
You have endowed me
With something more than I can swallow.
I do not pretend to understand
The pattern of your handiwork
Save that in a mysterious way
It helps me to magnify you.
You have wrought wonders in me, Lord,
No slim volume would suffice
To contain the Litany of your praise.
But perhaps a booklet,
For dare I call them, bones of contention?
For example, in the midst of tribulation

Was it quite necessary, Lord,
To allow my specs to nose-dive
And break on the bathroom floor?

SR, February 3rd, 1975

Coming up for the Third Time

Lord, in the last six days,
I have felt peculiarly plaintive,
Strength seems to be ebbing away,
My tale is a tale of woe.
Now in the midst of a melancholy moment
Preoccupation about pain
And thoughts squandered about swallowing,
I realise that I am
A man of little faith
And it is certainly true
That if Christ were to beckon me
Across the waves, immediately
I should begin to sink
Through sheer lack of confidence.
Lord, confirm me in the faith
Each time you come with comfort
As the bread of life, then
I shall realise that the Divine Strength
Is not ebbing away,
But gathering in intensity.

SR, February 7th, 1975

Sleepiness

Peter sleeps,
Simple statement
Comparable to
Sidney slumbers.
Lord, you have entangled me
In a torpor compulsive.

Could you not watch one hour?
My sleepiness is not of my own seeking
But I do feel a sense of guilt
When I sleep before Mass is ended
Or when eyelids droop
Halfway through the Our Father.
Lord, in the Gospels we see you sleep.
Even in the midst of a raging storm
You rebuked Peter, not for sleeping
But for lack of faith.
Could I not watch for one half-hour?
Lord, could it be possible
That you aid and abet me in sleep?

SR, February 16th, 1975

Lost Property

Priceless is that which I have lost,
Priceless because irretrievable.
Two days at least seemed
To have passed me by
In a fortnight of existence.
Rather uncanny
To think that yesterday is today
And today is yesterday.
But the Hospice has given reassurance
As well as sustenance,
Has given me twelve large hampers
Duly strained and liquidised.
The Bread of Life here below,
The great supper is awaiting
Ever awaiting.

SR, February 24th, 1975

Sidney died in the morning of 1st March 1975.

11

Life Has A Pattern

Cicely Saunders

Mr Brooks was sitting by his bed in one of the small number of single rooms at St. Christopher's Hospice. Now 63, he had, for many years, been a firefighter in London. It was January 1975 and he had been admitted two weeks before with an ulcerated and offensive recurrence of a carcinoma of the floor of his mouth. He had had surgery four and a half years earlier, followed by radiotherapy and chemotherapy. His previous hospital had now decided that further treatment of this nature was inappropriate and had asked the Hospice for admission to alleviate his terminal distress. His pain was by now well controlled, and the odour, previously his greatest distress and humiliation, no longer noticeable. We greeted each other, and after he had reported that his previous symptoms were under control, we went on talking.

'What do you do with yourself all day?'

'I read a bit and watch television; my wife and daughter spend a lot of time visiting me.'

'Do you get bored?'

'No. I am contented – all my life I've been, as you might call it, succouring people, helping others; now I am on the receiving end.'

'Do you find that hard?'

'No – I don't now – life has a pattern.'

A similar change of attitude in an elderly patient can be seen in the notes various members of staff made in the course of conversations with Mrs D, aged 82, who was with us from November 22nd 1974 to January 12th 1975.

24 November: 'I've accepted giving up my job – and then my home. I can bear the legs but I *can't* accept losing strength in my hands.' She knew she was not immortal but didn't feel eighty-two and could only look at acceptance bit by bit.

25 November: 'I see absolutely no purpose in my living. My body cannot stand nourishing. I have no reason to live. Yes, I have friends and this is a wonderful place, but what's the use in my going on?'

26 November: 'I'm not afraid to go. I've had a good life.'

19 December: 'I realise I'm dying. It's hard to accept but I do accept it. I'm not half as frightened as I was.'

21 December: 'I know what's happening – I am very happy – I don't worry any more. You couldn't help but be happy here. I am all right.'

Her physical condition was deteriorating, yet her outlook was developing all the time. Once she reached acceptance she did not lose it again. A few days before her death, three weeks after the last entry, she was overheard discussing the world to come with her friend, the long-stay patient in the next bed.

'Wouldn't it be good if we both went together,' she was heard to say, and the subsequent conversation made it plain that their expectation was to go to a place of excitement and interest. In fact, Mrs D died thirty-six hours after her friend, staying long enough to comfort the nurses and the many friends of that much-loved patient.

'Life has a pattern,' Mr Brooks had said and no one meeting him could doubt that this pattern had been accepted or that the acceptance had enabled good to emerge from what was indeed a desperately hard situation. Those who meet and listen to such people as Mr Brooks and Mrs D have seen repeatedly how much strength there is in accepted weakness and how often it is the person who is 'on the receiving end' who is giving courage to those around him or her.

Mr Brooks died five days after his sixty-fourth birthday. His wife had prepared a small celebration and came in to find that, according to Hospice custom, a birthday cake and party had been organised by the ward. The party continued for much of the day. I was away but was told about it afterwards by Mrs Brooks. She said, 'Everything that went before and anything that may come after will be worth it for that day.'

Photographs taken at the party show much of what St. Christopher's means for the staff, too, and what enables them to continue with such work at the level of caring demanded and given.

'Efficiency is very comforting,' said one relative. It is comforting to the family and also comforting to the staff to see pain relieved and relationships reaffirmed. Much weariness and mental suffering may still remain but it is deeply rewarding to meet people who are making such achievements out of life's pattern and to join in such occasions. We cannot take away the whole hard thing that is happening, but celebration is still an important part of life, and each Hospice occasion is a salute to this kind of courage. There is no need for the staff to idealise their patients, the daily reality of troubles accepted and overcome is enough. Neither patients, families, nor staff are protected from sadness, but in sharing it as they do they find that living and dying well are linked together and are constantly opening up new and creative possibilities.

12

Goodbye, Dot

Dot Flack

Dot Flack has been an Enrolled Nurse at St. Christopher's since July 1973.

Mrs Gabriele J, of German nationality, was born of a Jewish father and brought up in Nazi Germany, where most of the family were exterminated. But she escaped to this country where she met and married her English husband, becoming a schoolteacher in Gloucestershire, where she taught German.

She first realised something was wrong in January, 1973, when suddenly one morning she awoke to find she had great difficulty in walking. She went to her GP. Blood tests and X-rays were taken. These revealed carcinoma of the breast with spread to the bones. Her disease being so widespread it was considered advisable only to remove both ovaries – with a good response at first to this palliative operation.

She then returned to work on steroids and led a completely normal life until August, 1975, when the steroids had to be increased to their maximum dose (because of difficulty with walking and increased pain). In October, 1975, Mrs J was admitted to a local hospital and a further operation was performed. There she became very ill and was transferred to a London hospital, where she then received replacement therapy and radiotherapy to her spine and pelvis, and very heavy bouts of nausea and vomiting were controlled. By this time Mrs J was unable to walk at all and had much pain.

She was transferred to St. Christopher's in March, 1976. I remember the morning she was admitted – Gabby was an attractive young-looking 52, with very rosy cheeks, long dark hair worn in a ponytail and a ready smile for everyone. In fact she looked more healthy than the majority of nurses and doctors. But under the exterior was a small lady with a lot of thoracic and back pain. She was still getting occasional nausea and vomiting and her pain was so severe she could not reach out to her locker. She settled in well but was a bit demanding to begin with. After being at St. Christopher's for two days her pain was under control. We were able first of all to start getting her up into a chair and a week later got her walking with the help of nurses and later the physiotherapists helped her with a zimmer frame. It was nothing to see her walk past us in the corridor. Then on June 18th this year Mrs J went home with her husband for a long weekend to Gloucestershire. She also went home for another long weekend on July 2nd. But two days later Gabby was sitting on the side of her bed at the Hospice when she felt a vertebra collapse. She was confined to bed for two days, then was allowed up again. She was taken to her previous hospital (each time by her husband in their own car) for five more treatments of radiotherapy. Once again she reacted to her treatment with nausea and vomiting and was looking and feeling very poorly.

Three days later I went to see her and she was looking much brighter. I mentioned that I was going to speak at the Hospice's annual general meeting and that I should like to talk about her. Her face lit up and she looked very excited, then went on to talk to me for an hour and a half. Gabby was always extremely helpful in welcoming and talking to the many visitors who come to St. Christopher's from all over the world. She also translated German letters for Dr Saunders and responded greatly to any kind of teaching with the nurses and students and in fact has written a report on 'Patients as Teachers' for St. Christopher's annual report. Indeed we have gained as much from Gabby as she had gained from us.

On Thursday of last week at 23.45 Gabby awoke feeling and looking ill – very cold and clammy and, in fact, she had some bleeding. She was given an injection and soon fell asleep.

Then last Friday morning she had a further bleed and the same drugs were repeated. In the afternoon I went to sit with Gabby and her husband. I asked her how she felt and she said, 'I'm all right. It's my husband you've got to look after now.' And although she was extremely ill she was still aware. It was just as though she was trying to teach us how to die and at the same time was trying to take it all in herself. As I was leaving I kissed her and said, 'Bye, bye, God bless. See you soon, Gabby.' She replied 'Goodbye, Dot. Thank you very much for all you've done. Goodbye.'

Gabby died very peacefully at 7.10 last Sunday morning.

13

Mr K and Mr B

Ruth Noble

Ruth Noble was a Ward Sister and altogether at the Hospice from October 1973 to September 1979.

Mr K, a single man of 50, was admitted to St. Christopher's early in May 1977 with a carcinoma of the gullet for which a palliative operation had been performed. He also had a history of obsessional neurosis and some years before had had a prefrontal leucotomy which had helped him greatly. (He talked freely about this.) He had held a job in the Civil Service until recently and came to us because his elderly mother, who had arthritis, could not manage to look after him any longer, much as she wanted to.

Mr K was a talkative, well-liked man, independent to the point of obstinacy. He walked around the ward and liked to talk with the other patients and quickly made friends with the man in the next bed, Mr B, a 'loner' who had already been in the ward many months. Mr K discovered that they had a common interest in gardening. Mr B rarely spoke and never called folk by name, but Mr K seemed to draw him out. He made sure that Mr K never missed the steward's paper round and when Mr K was very ill and sleepy but still refusing help with his meals, he actually used his name, unheard of before, as he was falling asleep into his dinner.

At one point during his stay with us Mr K had two aims in life. One was to go by himself to buy a particularly expensive electric shaver from a special shop in Central London and the other was to be confirmed. A compromise was reached, and a volunteer drove him to London with a nurse to accompany him. He came back very pleased with himself and added the charging of his razor to all the other preparations that he went through carefully each night. The last dose of his drugs often had to be held up until everything was in exact order.

Each week Mr K had joined in the ward Communion service and after several talks with the assistant chaplain he asked to be confirmed. The Bishop came at short notice and Mr K prepared himself meticulously, carefully going over the words he had to say. He appeared in a smart suit and his mother, friends and ward and other Hospice staff joined him in an intensely moving service.

At the beginning of his stay Mr K made various indirect remarks about his illness to the nurses but asked no questions of the doctors until, one weekend, he decided that the time had come. Questions and answers went carefully and repeatedly round the point till finally he said, 'That means I don't have too long.' He talked about his confirmation as 'Just a cry for help' and he still wanted help to trust and relax. He wanted to talk to his mother at once and this was arranged and seemed to be a help to them both. After this, as Mr K became more ill, he was in turn more peaceful and then once again overwhelmed by obsessional restlessness. Nine days before he died his wanderings took him down to the Playgroup where he was found teaching the smallest children to tell the time on their model clock. Next day he cleared his locker and took a large bag of sweets and chocolate bars down to the children.

He gradually became more drowsy but was determined as ever to do things for himself. Two days before he died, when he could hardly stand, he made up his mind to walk to the bathroom. With a nurse on each arm and another close by he made it. That afternoon he attended a concert in the dining room but was persuaded to go in his bed.

After this he consented at last to be turned comfortably on

his side in bed and slipped into unconsciousness. He died in his sleep next day.

Two days later, Mr B had a sudden turn for the worse and unexpectedly died.

14

A Matter of Morale

Ted Holden

Ted Holden suffered from advanced motor neurone disease which left him totally paralysed, apart from some movement of his head. He wrote this article, which originally appeared in the *Nursing Times* in June 1980, using a typewriter linked to Possum equipment. Ted was in St. Christopher's from October 1976 to April 1982 and throughout that time was a wise and objective friend and supporter for many of those around him. Like the other three patients with motor neurone disease in this collection, he died very peacefully after a brief deterioration in his condition.

It would be silly and misleading to pretend that being almost totally dependent on others for anything requiring physical movement is a condition which is easy to accept. When speaking is also a problem the difficulties multiply and of course there is the awareness that however much one tries the slow but steady erosion will go on.

How one reacts is entirely up to the individual. It is within the compass of one's own philosophy and mental attitude, and here at St. Christopher's the care and support is so good that with a reasonable determination not to indulge one's tendencies to self-pity, it is not too difficult to sustain an acceptable quality of life.

What is beyond one's own capacity and therefore more depressing is the effect of a long illness on the family, especially the wife or husband. Without the sustenance of hope it is an experience of truly unimaginable trauma for which it is impossible to avoid a feeling of responsibility bordering on guilt. It is no use telling yourself that such thinking is stupid, there is a sort of truth in it. To die causes grief, but this softens and life can gradually be rebuilt. To keep everyone on the rack year after year watching you become an immobile skeleton is something different.

The point I am trying to make is that the illness is physical but given adequate help it is not too difficult to cope with. It is the emotional and mental stresses which are more of a problem.

An established routine, not rigid but encompassing the daily needs, is important. This would eliminate the irritation of having to repeat the struggle to be understood for simple, predictable and constantly recurring things. Rapid staff changes are a real problem. It is helpful if they can be filtered in gradually with assistance as far as possible. That way mutual confidence is more quickly established. It is common for new people to be so tense that they become incapable of normal comprehension.

Visitors are very important. Family support is a thing of priceless value. I am lucky. My wife visits frequently and regularly and the rest of the family come as often as they can, which is quite a lot. There is no doubt that their contribution is made easier and greater by a warm, relaxed and friendly atmosphere in the ward. Then there are visits from one or two friends and I get a few games of chess.

In terms of time, the hours occupied by or with visitors are a small proportion of the day. The greater value is to morale, and boredom can hardly exist if morale is high. Obviously and naturally my wife's visits have the greatest impact, but our very closeness means that we can more easily hurt each other and so we do have our problems, but we keep trying and, considering the strains and tensions, we manage pretty well. One must accept that human relationships are tricky at the best of times; to suppose perfect harmony can be achieved at all times is to expect miracles.

I believe that the main problem is simply to expect too much. One spends hours in eager anticipation which creates an oversensitive reaction to anything which falls short of expectation. The disappointment leads to poor communication and misunderstanding and as one realises that the mood is set and one is fully aware of the fundamental stupidity of it all, frustration, anger and remorse ensure that there is little prospect of recovery. What is sad is that you can do nothing until the next meeting which can be a long, long time. But one has to keep things in perspective and the good far outweighs the bad and the ugly. Apart from official visitors I get enormous help from members of the staff who spend a great deal of time with me when work permits. This is not only pleasant in itself but gives a feeling of being part of the community.

Boredom is probably the most difficult thing to counter and obviously much depends on the attitude of the individual, but a lack of self motivation does not indicate a lack of need. The alleviation of boredom in my case is simplified to some extent by the fact that because I am not able to do anything for myself I am not alone as much as I would otherwise be. The routine of eating, drinking, bathing, washing, getting up, going to bed, even the attention to the baser requirements of nature can all be pleasant interludes.

It was of course much easier before my speech became so badly affected, partly because I am robbed of initiative and partly because people tend to shy away either from nervousness or embarrassment. It is an extraordinary fact that so many people believe that because you are unable to talk you either can't or don't want to listen and anyway a one-way conversation is difficult to sustain. In truth, the less one is able to communicate the greater is the need. Without the contact enforced by physical needs one could become so isolated that there would be a natural and progressive withdrawal.

Loneliness is not so much a matter of being alone as of not belonging. Everyone needs person-to-person contact. Obviously time is a factor but by no means the main one. Unless there are mutual interests a specific visit can be embarrassing. Much more important is the general atmosphere. To be included in conversations in your presence, a smile, a nod, a wave, any socially acceptable gesture takes little effort and no time. To be looked through or ignored is not very warming. I wonder why so many doctors and nurses fail to understand such simple psychology.

I rarely feel lonely because although I am alone for many hours I always have the feeling of belonging. So one way or another I do pretty well for companionship. What is so good is that it is all free and easy. People just drop in for a chat or to give me the latest ward news and, dare I say it, even the occasional moan. Unless they are very good actors I have the feeling that, mostly, they come because they want to, which is good for my ego.

Despite this seemingly hectic social life there remain around seven or eight hours a day when I have to occupy myself and I am reminded of the old saying 'sometimes I sits and thinks and sometimes I just sits.' I have Possum equipment which gives me control of radio, television and the typewriter. The typewriter is a great boon. Apart from the obvious aid in communication which is invaluable, it demands great concentration and application, and is therefore positive, whereas the radio and television are passive and in themselves boring. Yet even when you are not really paying attention they provide a sort of companionship.

Before I was ill I was not too much concerned with my immediate surroundings. Now they matter very much and could hardly be better. Through the large windows I can look out at the weather – which is not half as bad as it is reputed to be – and a variety of trees, beautiful and interesting throughout the year. I have always loved trees and I have a large poster of a birch forest on the wall which, when the light is right, comes to life and is really beautiful. Everywhere I look there are flowers and plants, posters and cards and of course photographs: all bright and interesting, mostly cheering, occasionally sad, but never boring.

Although sustaining the maximum level of interest is always going to be a very personal and individual matter, there are many factors common to all. Everyone will benefit from bright and cheerful surroundings – everyone needs to feel wanted and needs help. All the background needs are basically the same.

Having established the right climate, it should not be too difficult to discover what the individual interests are. It will not be much use if the patient is simply asked, 'What would you like to do?' He or she will have no idea what is possible, available, attainable or reasonable, without being too demanding. You can find out what makes people tick through normal relaxed conversation, not by inquisition on an obviously limited timescale. Some will need more prompting than others but I have never met anyone not willing to talk about themselves given an interested audience.

While extraneous agencies like occupational therapists can help, the main contribution must come from the normal nursing staff. Maybe if we talk about mental welfare rather than boredom our approach would be better aimed and more meaningful. Fighting boredom conjures up images of knitting needles and banging away making things that no one wants and being organised, which is surely not what the average person wants. If we seek to create the best possible state of mind a positive approach is necessary, but how?

It seems illogical that the only people in hospital who have no training for the occupation are the patients. Would it not make sense to accept that anyone landed in a new and strange environment needs some sort of instruction to help him to fit in and take advantage of the enormous wealth of kindness, generosity, and good will, readily given by all staff?

What the patient has to understand is that although these are rather special people they are people with normal human feelings and responses. They do a very demanding job, work lousy hours for scandalous wages and have their share of trials and tribulations in their private lives. All patients are grateful for the care they get but many do not realise how much their own behaviour can contribute to their own and everyone's well-being.

When I suggest that patients could be taught I do not envisage anything overt, but judicious, friendly chats could achieve a great deal. Every patient has the right to know the what, why and the wherefore about everything from normal routine to his personal treatment and condition. No patient has the right to be constantly complaining, ill mannered, discourteous, jealous, selfish, thoughtless, all the petty things which make *us* so unattractive and will be counter-productive in our relationships with staff, relatives and everyone else. The basic lesson is simple, the greatest act of self-interest is to be as unselfish as possible.

The emphasis of my comment has been on attitudes and emotions because I felt that, although my views may seem to be very personal, there is much that is common ground to all patients. 'Coming to terms with your illness' is a phrase much used and I wonder what people think the process is. Do they believe that at some point you say to yourself, 'Look, you are in a pickle, but just pull yourself together, make the best of a bad job, and, apart from the odd lapse, you will be all right.' It is not like that. It is a day-to-day effort to adjust and adapt to a declining capability.

Panacea

Night after night
day after day
I lie in my bed
or sit in my chair
motionless
more or less
but not in my mind
it weightless and unrestrained
conjures with memories dreams and fantasies
richer by far than all your realities
when sport was physical
I was average
now only superlatives

can describe my performances
playing for England
I open the batting
the West Indies bowlers
are Roberts and Holding
the first ball a bouncer
I hook for six
Roberts not used to this
thinks it a fluke
and bowls me another
with easy grace and a roll of the wrists
it is flicked away and goes
like a bullet to the boundary
now he will be angry
and attempt to york me
I am ready
As he delivers I move forward
slightly
With a full swing of the bat
and perfect timing the contact
produces that wonderful sound that
only cricketers understand
and thinking of sounds
my mind fills with memories
the dreams recede
content as only lovers can be
we lie side by side in the dark
which only the firelight breaks
and listen to gentle ballads
of Nat King Cole or Frank Sinatra
Peggy Lee and the fabulous Ella
The floor is hard but we are aware
of no discomfort
hardly moving
rarely talking
alert only to the sensuous pleasure
of the music and our own presence

A Matter of Morale

am I different or do we all
best remember happiness
I know it's only self defence
so what? It's still nice, ain't it.

Ted Holden

15

A Quality of Dying

Ann Murley

Mrs Murley's mother, Mrs Mary Barton, was a patient at St. Christopher's from December 1981 to April 1982.

In writing the following I hope to share with the reader my feelings and experiences of family tragedy in the loss of two very dear parents, within a short space of time, and in totally different ways. Death, although so final and tragic, need not be as traumatic as people believe, as is highlighted in the case of my mother's death, which was so very peaceful at the end and an experience I was privileged to share with her.

My father died very suddenly – he was 64. He went into hospital for what seemed a fairly routine gallbladder operation, but while under the anaesthetic he had a massive heart attack and was immediately removed to the intensive care unit in a critical condition.

I visited him with my mother and for a time he regained consciousness and recognised us. He was surrounded by machines, wires, tubes, drips and the medical equipment used when treating patients with severe heart conditions. We sat with him, holding his hand, and the nurses encouraged us to speak to him as, although he appeared to be in a deep sleep, we were assured that he could hear us and that maybe he would respond by the squeeze of a hand or the flutter of an eyelash.

We were never once consulted by a doctor, although a group of doctors looked in on him once or twice. The nurses were very kind but it was so clinical and impersonal and Dad was on the receiving end of it all and dying.

He died while we were in the waiting-room.

Life has to continue after someone you have loved dies – he or she is at peace but it is the family who are left in a state of turmoil, grief and confusion. It is the family who are left to pick up the pieces and manage as best they can. In this case, my mother had to come to terms with living the rest of her life alone with memories going back nearly a lifetime. We all supported her and she coped admirably as only she could. Mum was a very capable person, always supportive in our crises. This was her crisis, and my sister Christine, brother Richard and I were there to share her sadness, and to offer what support and comfort we could.

During the months following Dad's death, Mum busied herself with various activities, especially at her Church. She rejoined pottery classes and met Tom who was later to prove an invaluable close friend.

During the months following it seemed to me that Mum was losing weight and not eating properly. This we put down to the traumatic nature of recent events, and the grief that she was obviously experiencing. However, when she went to America some weeks later for a short holiday, and had to return somewhat unexpectedly because she felt so unwell, we knew it was something more serious. The doctor who was consulted in America diagnosed an aneurysm of the aorta, a very serious condition, and it was imperative that she receive medical attention in this country immediately. This I arranged and within two days of returning home Mum was in a London hospital undergoing tests.

We could only try and imagine what Mum must have been feeling during those days of endless tests. We ourselves were extremely worried and frightened. Eventually it was established that it was not an aneurysm that was causing the trouble but cancer, that dreaded illness that either meant weeks of horrible treatment or death. Just how far the cancer had spread had not been ascertained and there were more tests. It was then decided to remove the spleen, at the same time giving the doctors an opportunity of finding out exactly what was happening. Mum came through the operation well and I spent many hours with her afterwards. It was important that I was close to her at this time for I loved her so much; we had a very special relationship and I wanted her to feel that I was there to comfort her as much as possible.

Tom was a constant visitor at the hospital, as were family and friends, many of whom were members of Mum's Church and were able to provide her with spiritual comfort.

Removing the spleen had in fact helped Mum's discomfort but had also proved that the cancer had spread and I was told that Mum had about two months to live. This was shattering news because, although I had known deep down that she was not going to get better, when the words are actually spoken, it seems so final and there is no hope left. The sadness and distress were unbearable, but in times of such crises, one receives an inner strength to cope. I realised now that I was going to lose Mum. If only there was something I could do, but sadly there was nothing except offer my love and to be there, supporting and caring during the short time she had left.

The doctor told Mum that there was nothing they could do for her and that her life was limited. We comforted her by holding her hand and putting our arms around her. Words were meaningless and there would be time to talk later.

The days went by and she recovered physically from the operation but mentally was very distressed. We spent many hours with her, matching our mood to hers, and we talked at length of our fears and anxieties. She was so brave, seeming to care only about how we were feeling.

The hospital would be discharging Mum as soon as she was feeling stronger and Richard, Mum and I were talking about what would happen when she was discharged, as we felt she would not be able to manage at home.

What happens to people who are discharged from hospital knowing that they are going to die? What provision is made for them? Not so long ago they would have gone home to die and been looked after by relatives, the whole burden of caring falling on the family. Presumably some still do, but we discussed the possibility of Mum's going into a hospice.

The most famous hospice and the one nearest to Mum's home was St. Christopher's in Sydenham and it was to that Hospice that Richard made approaches as to the procedure for admittance. Naturally this was discussed at great length with Mum and it was what she wanted, providing the best care for her during the last weeks.

Hospices are very special places and do much to ease the burden of dying, both for the patient and for the relatives. I had visited St. Christopher's a few years before, being shown around and talking to patients as part of my training as a Samaritan – befriending the dying. I can remember feeling very apprehensive and nervous at meeting and seeing people who had only a short time to live. I was so impressed with the nurses and the atmosphere of the Hospice. There was a feeling of peace and contentment with none of the medical equipment that had surrounded my father when he died. The rooms were light and airy and full of flowers. Some patients were up and the feelings of love, care and warmth were everywhere; death when it came would be dignified and peaceful. If Mum was going to die and spend her last days at St. Christopher's she would not suffer; there would be no pain and she would not be alone.

The formalities were completed between the hospital and the Hospice and a date arranged for Mum to be admitted. We could only try and imagine what she must have been feeling – she was going to a place to die, so final with no turning back, no second chance.

We all gave her as much support as is possible to give another person. She was a much loved mother and very respected among her friends and the members of her Church. Her faith in God was her anchor at this time and one to which she clung.

On the day she left hospital I arrived at 9 a.m., allowing

ample time for the ambulance that was going to take us to the Hospice. I helped Mum dress and packed her small case, including two beautiful miniature pewter bowls with fruit and flowers that had been given to her by a dear friend of mine, David, who cared so much for Mum. These little miniatures had travelled all over the hospital with Mum, on her various tests, in her dressing-gown pocket – she would have taken them into the operating theatre if possible – she thought so much of them.

We waited for the ambulance and by lunchtime were getting somewhat anxious and fidgety. Where was the blessed thing? The nurses did not seem to know. 'It could come any time,' they said. And so we waited and waited. By 4 p.m. I was so annoyed at the delay and seemingly lack of understanding that I telephoned the Hospice to explain the situation. They were very kind but said it was now too late to receive Mum as they preferred to receive their patients in the morning to settle them in and to ensure that they received the appropriate welcome in a relaxed atmosphere. This seemed reasonable to me, but the hospital's attitude was infuriating.

They suggested Mum should spend another night there, which I did not accept and demanded they ordered a hospital car so that I could take her home with me for the night. She had prepared herself to go to the Hospice and to keep her in the hospital seemed unfair and unkind; far better for her to spend the night in a warm caring environment. I would take her to the Hospice the following morning. On our arrival at my flat I made Mum comfortable. Tom came round later and we spent a quiet evening together, laughing a little and beginning to relax. Mum slept well for she must have been exhausted.

In the morning she said, 'Ann, I am glad it turned out this way – this has been much nicer and I have so enjoyed this time with you and I have slept so well.'

I too was pleased to have had the opportunity of spending time, however short, with her: it was a bonus.

The next morning was bitterly cold when we made our

way to St. Christopher's. My stomach was churning and I kept asking Mum if she was all right.

'Yes,' she said, 'I'm OK, just a little apprehensive.' I held her hand.

I drove round to the back of the Hospice and waiting for us were two nurses with a bed which had been warmed by hot-water bottles. There was also a wheelchair, but Mum walked from the car to the bed. We went up in the lift to the ward. Everyone was so kind and a lady doctor immediately appeared and introduced herself. I was then shown into her office and she spent about an hour with me, wanting to know all about Mum and the family situation. She had the medical notes from the hospital, but seemed more interested in me and how I was feeling. It was such a relief to speak to someone in the medical profession who knew what I was going through. The interview was conducted in an unhurried, calm atmosphere and I experienced then for the first time an inner peace. I had at last come to terms with the fact that Mum was going to die, but I also knew that she was going to die with dignity and with love and understanding.

The doctor said it was impossible to say exactly how long she had got to live, but that it would be weeks rather than months, and that it would be a gradual slipping away with no pain or undue suffering. She would just get weaker and weaker and death, when it came, would be peaceful.

We could visit the Hospice at any time of the day and would always be welcome. The whole atmosphere was so relaxed.

The doctor then spent some time with Mum and she invited me to be with them. She gave Mum a chance to talk about herself and her illness and her fears. Mum was able to speak quite freely about the events of the past months, including of course Dad's sudden death.

She asked the question, 'Exactly how long have I got, doctor?'

Again the doctor replied, 'Well let's say it is weeks, maybe a month or so but certainly not a year.'

They talked together about Mum's faith and the strength that she had been able to draw from it. Mum cried and we both held her hands; the doctor got down on her knees beside the bed and cradled Mum's head, comforting her. There would be no treatment, just drugs to help combat any discomfort and pain.

I stayed with Mum for a short time to settle her in and said I would visit again in the afternoon. I had some Christmas shopping to do, but most of all I needed a rest. I was very tired both mentally and physically.

There was a constant stream of visitors at the Hospice to see Mum. My cousin Ruth came over from America and Tom was always at her side. Family and friends came regularly. We bought her a portable radio and television with ear phones so she was able to listen without disturbing the other patients. She loved music and spent many hours listening to her favourite tapes. As each day went by she seemed to grow stronger and not weaker as we had originally thought. This, said the doctor, was because she was still recovering from the operation. She began to eat and enjoy her food again and looked better. She got up and chatted with those patients who were well enough and sat with those who were not. The lady in the bed next to Mum died soon after Mum went into the Hospice. People were dying. You could not get away from that fact, but Mum certainly did not seem as though she was going to die yet.

Christmas was drawing nearer and the doctor asked me if I would like to have Mum home for Christmas. She was certainly well enough and it would be lovely to have her. She was overjoyed at the prospect, as she had entered the Hospice with the accepted knowledge that she would not come home again, so this news was very exciting – another bonus.

It would be a very special Christmas for all of us, her last Christmas and one which we would never forget. I fetched her on Christmas Eve knowing that if anything went wrong we were to return immediately.

My flat was decorated with lots of cards, holly and a

Christmas tree; I always love Christmas Eve and this one was especially nice.

My children had got their Grandma some presents and we all opened them together around the tree on Christmas morning. It was a little difficult to know what to give her, but talcs, soaps, Jackson's teas and perfume seemed to go down well. My son, Nikolas, gave Mum a very pretty tissue-box cover which was very sensible as she was able to keep it by her bed.

I had to keep busy to stop crying, for if I cried then I knew Mum would cry and then the children. So I put on a brave face, which was not too difficult in the circumstances as the day was perfect and, despite Dad's not being there, was one of the best Christmases we had ever had. We were all conscious of the fact that this would be Mum's last and we so wanted it to be a happy occasion, and it was. The family arrived on Christmas afternoon and Tom turned up in time for tea. Boxing Day was just as perfect and Mum was enjoying herself and the goodies that are around at Christmas time. Tom was able to stay with us as well.

Thus Christmas came and went and, because Mum was so happy at being home with us all and keeping fairly well, we thought it would be nice for her to stay at home for another week or so. The Hospice agreed and I collected another supply of medication for her. Unfortunately I had to return to work, but Mum spent her days resting and seeing her visitors, with Tom staying as often as he could.

Those days were very precious for us all. They were happy and we lived for each day, thankful for what they brought, not thinking too much of the future: no future for Mum, but certainly a future for us. She was so grateful for this time and I was able to care for her, settling her down at night; she had a nasty bedsore that needed dressing and the Hospice told me how to do this. I also gave her limbs and back a massage which she found very soothing; this would help her to sleep and by the same token gave me a feeling of providing her with the comfort that she needed.

Eventually the time came for her to return to the Hospice and Tom took her back. We missed her, and the flat felt so empty. I wondered how long she would remain at the Hospice before dying; she obviously had some time left and somehow it did not seem right for her to return while enjoying being at home and appearing relatively well. After talking this over with the doctor, Mum was asked whether she would like to return to her own home. The sisters from the Hospice would call in regularly and she would only have to pick up the phone and help would arrive immediately should she need it. We were all a little apprehensive at whether she would be able to manage, but Mum clearly wanted to return, and we would help her as much as possible. Her house had not been lived in for some months so we set about making it as welcoming for her as we could.

It must have seemed quite amazing for Mum to walk through her own front door again, never having thought during those awful days in the hospital that she would return home. She was absolutely overjoyed at being there and settled down well, with the support of her family, Tom and the sisters from the Hospice. Tom eventually moved in with Mum and it was a comfort to me, and I'm sure to Richard and Christine, that she was not alone.

There was one moment for Mum that meant such a lot to her and that was when she drove her car for the first time since being ill, again achieving something she thought she would never do again. Another bonus, as was each day and each moment of her life.

How could Mum be dying, I asked myself; she was managing a little housework, cooking, shopping and she even helped me tidy the garden. I was so proud of her, quite frail, aware that for her life was so short, but enjoying all that every day brought. She would tire very easily, but gave in to it in the knowledge that she had had a good day.

There were bad days, of course, as Mum called them. Days when she felt very uncomfortable, days when she did not eat, days when she was depressed and cried, days when she must have longed to be well again. But she got through those days and then had some good days.

The Hospice decided, after one of Mum's check-ups, that they would give her steroids to help combat her uncomfortable feelings and give her an appetite. They certainly worked and gave Mum a feeling of well-being, but slowly over the weeks she was getting weaker. She was very distressed at the side-effects of the steroids. Her face started to swell, not very noticeably, but nevertheless causing embarrassment for her. She cut them down in the hope of controlling the swelling, which did in fact help, but it was a vicious circle for she began to feel ill again.

At the end of March, Tom decided that he would like to take Mum away for a few days to the Cotswolds. The weather was turning warmer and they both thought it would be a good idea to have a few days away together. Sadly it was not to be. Mum felt so ill and weak and could not enjoy the break; she was depressed and wanted to come home. Upon reflection it was probably a mistake; she was too ill to have travelled but it was a joint decision and one which they made, with the doctor's approval.

During the following days at home I spent many hours with Mum, talking and sometimes just holding her hand saying nothing. We talked about her dying; it was quite obvious that this was not far away now, and she knew it. She wanted to talk about her life and mentioned her own Mother's death on a number of occasions. She also said that when she had gone, I should always feel that I had done my very best for her and given her happiness in her last months; this was true, I feel exactly that. There was nothing more I could have done.

Mum was not afraid to die, for she had come to terms with it. Only two days before her death David said to her, 'You are privileged, Mary, you know you are dying and your peaceful acceptance is something I hope I experience when my time comes.' Lovely words for a very brave lady.

We now brought Mum's bed downstairs as she was too

weak to climb the stairs. We also moved the telephone near to her chair for convenience. One day I arrived at the house to find Mum trembling and shaking all over and obviously very distressed as she was unable to control her body. I had never seen her like this before and I went with her into the lounge and sat with her until the shaking had subsided and she had calmed down. She began to feel a little better and we talked. Talking was so important for both of us and we grew very close to each other during those days.

Richard and his wife, Janette, had gone away for a short holiday to Wales and were due back on the Saturday. On the Thursday before they came home, Mum was so weak that she went to bed. I was, by this time, staying with her and she was being visited by the sisters who showed me how to turn her in bed. Even though she was so frail, it was still difficult for me to turn and sit her up. A nurse trained in lifting and turning patients has no difficulty, but I obviously needed a little guidance and this they gave me. It was because of this that in later years I took a Red Cross course in nursing, learning the proper methods of looking after people who are in bed.

On the Friday she had a few visitors, including her sister from Watford. Her own GP and District Nurse also visited. Mum was sleeping a lot now; she would wake at times and have a little to eat and drink and a chat. She would then drift off to sleep again, very peaceful, calm and comfortable. Apart from the analgesics she was taking she had no other drugs; these seemed to keep her comfortable and she relied upon them.

On Saturday morning, after I had made her comfortable, she slept and I read for a while. After lunch the doctor visited and the sisters from the Hospice. We talked in the other room about Mum's condition, which they felt was now critical and that her death was imminent. They asked me if I needed any other help, but I was managing and quite able to cope.

Richard and Janette arrived home during Saturday afternoon. I was so pleased to see them, for I wanted them to be home before Mum died. They spent some hours with her. Mum would waken periodically and ask us if we were all right.

'Yes,' we said, 'How are you?'

'Fine,' she said, 'I feel so sleepy and relaxed, you don't mind if I keep drifting off, do you.'

My children also visited her during the early evening. She was so pleased to see them. They did not stay long, but long enough to be with their Grandma and to be held and kissed by her and to say their goodbyes.

Everybody had gone and I was waiting for the District Nurse to come and settle Mum down for the night, but she did not arrive and by about 10 p.m. Mum needed to be settled and wanted to go to sleep. She was a little restless so I washed her and massaged her limbs, cleaned her mouth, brushed her hair and gave her the medication. I asked her if she wanted me to stay with her but she said, 'No, Ann, you go upstairs and get some sleep.'

This I did, leaving her with a little bell to ring if she wanted me. I must have slept for a while, but was awoken by a strange sound. I immediately rushed downstairs and found Mum slumped right down in the bed and breathing rather strenuously. I tried to make her more comfortable and she asked for a drink. I said I would stay with her, but she said she would be all right and to go back to bed, so rather reluctantly I went; she seemed to be almost asleep again, and I knew that instinct would tell me if she needed me.

Perhaps two hours passed and I felt very uneasy. I went downstairs again and Mum's breathing was very much worse. I immediately phoned the Hospice and told them that I thought Mum had very little time left and that her breathing was very bad. They reassured me and said they would contact the sister on call who would come out immediately.

I went back to Mum and sat with her, holding her hand. I can remember her saying in a very faint voice, 'It won't be long now, Ann, don't be afraid.'

I wasn't afraid, and when she died, half an hour later, before the sister arrived, it was the most peaceful experience I had ever shared with her. Our very last moments together.

As one of Mum's friends said afterwards at the funeral, 'Mary couldn't teach us how to live, but she taught us how to die.'

How very true those words were and how privileged I was to be with her at the end.

In my garden I have a plant given to me by Mother a few weeks before her death. Every spring it comes to life no matter how hard the winter has been, and is a reminder that for me Mum's memory will never fade.

It was five years before I felt able, or indeed wanted, to write my account of her dying. The weeks and months following her death were very painful for me. Grief is such a desolate thing. There is nothing that can be done to bring back someone you have loved, but I was very much aware during those months, and even now still am, of the help that we received from the Hospice which achieved a very special quality of life for Mum during her last weeks. She was active until three days before she died, enjoying what she could, and together we shared some very precious moments.

I shall always remember our closeness during her final months and that she 'lived until she died', made possible by the love I had for her, the care of the Hospice and, above all Mum's final acceptance of death, something which, sadly, not everyone is able to do. Everyone understands the need for a quality of life, but does everyone understand the need for a quality of death?

If death were predictable we should all be prepared. Many people die suddenly, like my Father, with no warning, no time to prepare. Perhaps easy for them, but to be prepared and accept is surely the ultimate when faced with inevitable death. With the hospices' specialist care there is *hope* for the terminally ill, in coming to terms with death in the gentlest possible way.

As time passes my grief becomes more bearable and indeed

I feel a sense of achievement in having written all this down. I feel a release and happiness at having been able to express and record my experiences of death and I hope that reading this may bring to others the feelings of peace and dignity which surrounded Mother during her final days. We all received such support and care from the sisters of the Hospice who were always there when we needed them. They do such marvellous work and I wish them continued success. Only those who pass through their doors will know how they are able to make death both dignified and peaceful for the terminally ill and more bearable for those who are left behind.

16

Control and Trust

Anne Morrison

Anne Morrison is a Ward Sister at St. Christopher's.
Jean was a patient between November 1981 and early
1982. The Pilgrim Club meets every month and is a
place where the bereaved can come to share and begin
to learn how to come to terms with their loss.

Jean was admitted to St. Christopher's late in November 1981.
She was a small attractive woman of 44, and her diagnosis
was cancer of the rectum. The disease had spread to her brain,
spine and lungs and she was in severe pain. Her GP had
requested her admission to us for control of pain.

Jean's previous admission to hospital, where surgery had
been carried out, had left her apprehensive, owing mainly to
the lack of information given. She had presumed that the
'ulcer' in the bowel had been healed by the operation, but
found it difficult to understand why she was becoming progressively weaker. Even after discharge Jean had felt no better
and the pain was becoming worse. Visits to the hospital
out-patients gave no relief, just reassurance that all was well,
and more painkillers.

Jean was part of a large Irish Catholic family. Her husband,
Jim, is a publican and there are two sons, aged 16 and 19. Her
mother and father are still alive and she has three sisters and
a brother. They all visited frequently and eventually spent
most of their days here. Their own Catholic priest was also a
regular visitor.

Jean was frightened and apprehensive on admission, in a lot
of pain and asking probing questions about her condition.

She had not been told the nature of her illness until now. She was initially seen together with her husband and sister, but later on she was often seen alone whenever she needed to talk, and gradually she began to realise the serious nature of her illness. We gave her the company and support she so frequently needed while coming to terms with her prognosis, and her problems and fears were discussed carefully and honestly.

Over the next few days Jean's pain was fully controlled on a morphine mixture. Now aware of her disease and prognosis, she said she was not afraid of dying but wanted as much time with her family as possible.

Because of this and her age it was decided to give Jean glucocorticosteroids. Serious consideration is given before starting these tablets. They often have the ability to give an improvement in general condition for a limited period, so in Jean's case this seemed the correct decision. We of course discussed this with her and her family and she agreed to try them.

After several days Jean's strength and appetite had improved considerably, so much so that she asked to go home. This was readily agreed to and, after a successful trial weekend at home, she was discharged two weeks after admission to the joint care of her GP and our own out-patients' clinic, who agreed to phone Jean regularly as she lived out of our visiting area. Jean spent a very successful six weeks at home.

Christmas was spent with all the family present. She had thoroughly exhausted herself cooking and cleaning, but assured us she had enjoyed herself immensely.

Jean was seen at regular periods in the out-patient clinic. She continued to gain weight and looked well. When she came to the clinic she would also take the opportunity to visit the ward, telling us about her progress and chatting to patients that she knew.

In early January, however, we did notice that she was looking more tired, and the steroid medication was starting to be less effective. In mid-January Jean was seen again in the clinic, she was feeling unwell, was drowsy, and vomiting was now a problem. Jim was worried and tired and requesting Jean's admission. She didn't want to come in, but by now she knew and trusted us and accepted our advice. Vomiting was quickly brought under control with medication, but it was obvious to us and her family that the disease had progressed and she was much less well. Her steroid therapy was therefore reduced.

Jean's deteriorating condition was explained to her husband and the rest of the family, and we made ourselves available at all times to comfort and support them. This was a particularly sad time for Jean's mother; she was losing her eldest daughter and it was often difficult to console her.

Our social worker maintained a very good rapport with Jean's two sons and we encouraged them to visit and be with their mother as often as possible.

A further weekend at home was requested, but this time Jean returned early, eager to be back in secure surroundings. She was now showing signs of obstruction, meaning that the disease had invaded a great deal of the bowel. Pain was still successfully controlled with an increase in medication, and she spent more and more time sleeping, surrounded by members of her family. This crisis had brought them closer together than ever, supported by their strong Catholic faith and the nursing staff.

Jean's condition deteriorated rapidly after this and she died peacefully with her husband, sons and sister present.

Jim visited us several months after Jean's death; he was accompanied by his two sons. He presented us with a cheque from himself and the regular customers of his pub, it was obviously a very emotional moment for him and the boys.

He now keeps in regular contact with the ward staff, attends our Pilgrim Club and remains one of our best supporters.

17

Mr Soames Soldiers On

Lynn Mackay

Lynn Mackay (who became Lynn Hill) was a Ward
Sister and at St. Christopher's for eight years.

Mr Soames was admitted to Nuffield Ward, accompanied by
his adopted daughter, on February 16th, 1981. Fifty-seven
years old, Baptist, he had a diagnosis of multiple myeloma.

This was a slightly unusual case in so far that his wife
was also admitted on the same day to Princess Alexandra
Ward suffering from advanced carcinoma of the colon. Much
checking, phone calls to the doctors and social workers in
charge of both cases were undertaken by matron and our ad-
missions secretary, Mrs Wright. This was to make certain if St.
Christopher's admitted both Mr and Mrs Soames there would
be continuing care elsewhere for Mr Soames following his
wife's death, as he was not thought to be in the terminal stage
of his illness.

Mr Soames's problems first started in September 1980,
when he began suffering considerable back pain. In December
1980 he attended an out-patient appointment at a London
hospital where an X-ray showed that his spine had collapsed
at the first lumbar vertebra, and he was admitted immediately
for further investigation. Following these investigations a
diagnosis of myeloma was made.

Mr Soames was told that he had a malignant bone tumour.
Being the sort of person he was, he wanted to know the
correct name for the disease and then promptly took himself

off to read all about it. He may well have read something like the following:

'In this disease multiple tumours develop in bone. The tumours arise from plasma cells in various bones, especially the skull, spine, ribs and pelvis. As they grow they erode the bone, which gives way under pressure or strain with the production of deformity or spontaneous fracture. Tumours of similar cells are sometimes present in liver, spleen, kidneys or tonsil. The disease occurs in the later half of adult life. It is always fatal; about half the patients die within a year, a few live for more than five years.'

In January he was given his first course of cytotoxic therapy, intravenous cyclophosphamide. This was followed by a four-day admission to another hospital for radiotherapy to his spine. On his return to the original hospital he could just walk using a frame for support, which he had been unable to do previously. He also had an indwelling catheter at that time, much to his distress, as he was having urinary problems. His pain was said to be controlled on a mixture called aspirin and Nepenthe (opium) which he was taking every three hours.

In early February he was given his second course of intra-venous cytotoxic therapy. Mr Soames was coming to dread these days as he was always very nauseated and vomited during the treatment. He was also extremely low in spirits and depressed – not only over his own problems, but he could see his wife's condition was rapidly deteriorating. It was at this time the wheels were put into motion for the admission of them both to St. Christopher's.

During the first few days Mr Soames spent most of his time on Alex Ward with his wife, who was very ill. She died in the early part of the morning of February 19, only three days after their admission, and Mr Soames was with her.

Over the next few weeks we found our role changing. We were not only nurses but bereavement counsellors. Medically, at times, Mr Soames could prove to be a problem to the doctors. The pain in his back had returned with a vengeance. He quickly moved from doses of morphine 20mg four-hourly to 30mg, to 45mg four-hourly. At this dose he felt a little drowsy so the morphine was reduced to 30mg four-hourly but Butacote (phenylbutazone), which can work extremely well in bone pain, was added. Two of these tablets taken three times a day soon resulted in a much happier, pain-free Mr Soames.

The catheter by this time had been removed but Mr Soames seemed to suffer continually with infections in his urine and at times was passing blood. Constipation too seemed to be a never-ending cry. His mobility continued to improve with regular visits from the physiotherapists, and at times we thought he would eat us out of house and home!

He always wanted to be told the truth to any question he asked, and one day Dr Baines, the consultant, was put into the position of telling him what was going to be the most likely cause of death and how he was likely to die.

The third course of cytotoxic therapy was due. Mr Soames had become nauseated and wretched and generally felt he was back to square one. He asked if he could have any other form of treatment, preferably orally. The ward doctors consulted Dr Thelma Bates, consultant radiotherapist and oncologist at St. Thomas's Hospital. Dr Bates visits St. Christopher's four times a year to advise us on any radiotherapy or cytotoxic therapy problems we may have. She suggested melphalan which meant Mr Soames only took half a tablet daily for two weeks in every month. So with everyone's blessing we started this new treatment on April 4 with no side-effects.

Before all this we had desperately been trying to detach Mr Soames from our apron-strings. Two weekends at home with some support from his adopted son and daughter had not been regarded as a total success, and a two-week holiday in Brighton with his mother had resulted in his driving back to St. Christopher's after five days saying, 'Mother tried to tempt me with tasty dishes but it was no good', and then cried, 'I miss my wife so much.' Within two days of returning to St. Christopher's he was his old self again, and we were very aware that Mr Soames was making Nuffield Ward his home.

After much talking we finally gently persuaded Mr Soames that he should try a spell in his own home. On April 16 he was discharged under the care of the out-patient team.

It seems it was the right decision after all. Mr Soames really has never looked back! The out-patient sisters always seem to have great difficulty in contacting him as he is never at home.

The melphalan treatment has continued every month, and now Mr Soames rarely complains of pain – in fact he stopped taking morphine in June. The Butacote tablets were gradually reduced to one tablet twice a day, and following his last clinic visit he has stopped taking them altogether.

He gives a lot of time to working with the St. John Ambulance Brigade and in June did a sponsored roller-skating competition for them – he was roller-skating! In July he was on duty in The Mall for the Royal Wedding and this month he has been allowed to return to work full time.

So beware where you park in future because you may receive a ticket from Mr Soames. Yes, he is working full time as a traffic warden!

The latest news of Mr Soames, six years on, is that he is well but he has moved out of the district.

18

Sam

Lynn Hill (Mackay)

What do you do with a 71-year-old widowed man who has no living relatives, who suffers from a cancer in the lung, who has severe back pain, is independent and stubborn and his two loves in life are the local pub and Bell's whisky? This delightful problem arrived on Nuffield Ward in May 1983 and stayed with us for the next three months and will be remembered by the ward staff, and probably the staff of the local pub, as one of the 'characters' of St. Christopher's Hospice.

Sam's diagnosis had been made in May 1982 and after a short admission to a London hospital he had gone home to his very poor flat where he coped, refusing all help from the local services, until April 1983 when he was again admitted. This time Sam agreed he could no longer manage at home on his own as his illness had progressed. An application was made to the Hospice and Sam duly arrived.

I shall never forget my first meeting with this man. He was brought to the ward in a wheelchair dressed in a suit, a shirt covering his pyjama jacket and what became his famous trilby.

Sam was one of the most impossible people I have ever had to look after, but one had to admire him. He caused us a great many headaches and when I asked the ward staff about their memories of Sam I was barraged with the following things. Washing was one of the greatest fights of the day: in fact he just didn't. The nurses would report that Sam had yet again had a 'dry clean'. His clothes seemed to belong in the same category but eventually, after many arguments, he allowed them to be sent to the laundry.

The drug rounds were also a constant battle. Even after

careful observation, matchboxes full of tablets would be found – 'in case I need something later'. The doctors would spend their time each week listening to Sam's various complaints of pain, or swollen legs, or trouble with breathing – prescribe the appropriate drug for the problem – and then Sam would refuse to take it!

Meal times! Sam would never be awake for breakfast and would be out at lunch and supper times. We always saved his ordered meal – he would be furious if we hadn't – and then he would either eat it two or three hours later or store it in his locker! Every three or four days one of the nurses would have to go secretly through the locker and remove decomposing boiled eggs, chicken joints or fried fish. The highlight of Sam's day was to go to the betting shop and then on to the pub. When he first came he could slowly walk to these places, but as time went on, and Sam became more incapacitated, he progressed to catching the number 12 bus – which he eventually fell off – and then to the local taxi service.

The other patients in the ward found him useful when they wanted their bets placed and he kept the nurses supplied with biros to which he helped himself in the betting shop.

The pub was a much bigger problem. We gave up asking Sam to come in before the Hospice locked up. On more than one occasion the night staff had to help a rather intoxicated Sam to bed and give him two Panadol regularly the next morning for his hangover.

There are times as a Ward Sister when you have to be an ogre. Five days before Sam died I had to put my foot down and say he could not go to the pub. We had had several heated discussions during Sam's three months' stay but I think this was the worst, and how awful and mean I felt having to say it. The local taxi firm could no longer manage to get Sam in and out of the cabs because he was so immobile and the bar staff at the local were so busy and could not always give him the attention he needed. On several occasions some of the customers had to carry him to the toilet. It had to stop, and I had to do it, but after telling Sam he could drink as much as he wanted on the ward he said, 'It's not the drink, girl, it's the atmosphere,' and not even St. Christopher's could create that in the middle of Nuffield Ward.

Sam died peacefully five days later and only managed to get to the pub one more time.

As I have already said, he will never be forgotten by the ward staff but one of the best occasions was when he joined us at the annual barbecue/disco – 'Are you going to buy me a drink Sister?' How could I refuse?

19

You Don't Need Legs in Heaven

Peter Kaye

Dr Peter Kaye worked at St. Christopher's from 1983–5 and is now Medical Director of an NHS Continuing Care Unit.

Brian was a 37-year-old stockbroker's clerk. He had a spinal tumour that had paralysed both legs and also caused severe back pain. Despite having several different treatments and even having the spinal cord cut, he had suffered increasing pain for over six months and had very seriously considered suicide. He came to St. Christopher's in January 1985 and at first his pain was very difficult to control.

He was depressed with the constant pain and also felt his dependence on others was degrading. Above all, he was angry with God for his deterioration in the face of prayers for healing.

After several different forms of treatment his pain began to decrease. He was able to sit up for the first time without pain and take an interest in his hobby of making doll's house furniture.

Eventually he was able to work for several hours at a time and the ward occasionally reverberated to the noise of his miniature electric saw. His two sons, aged 7 and 10, visited him. One of them found it very difficult to express his feelings but was encouraged to do some painting and did a picture of heaven with many legless figures and animals and commented, 'You don't need legs in heaven, you float.'

Eventually Brian and his wife, Jenny, felt confident enough about his pain control to try some time back home. Brian was able to sit in his garden and enjoyed teaching his sons how to use the woodwork tools he had used since he was a boy.

His arms were getting weaker and he feared becoming totally helpless but he no longer felt suicidal and his strong faith in God had returned. He emphasised to us that he could only remain cheerful and positive if he knew his life was short. He had had two serious infections treated in the Hospice and then he made us promise that we would not give him antibiotics if the infection recurred. Brian wanted to be at home to see more of his two sons. His severe pain had stopped and Jenny was keen to care for him, but they were both frightened of the pain returning. Brian had a week at home, returned to the Hospice for two weeks and then felt able to return home altogether. He died peacefully at home three weeks later.

Brian hated his dependence but he remained defiant to the end. He selected the words for his own funeral and chose 'The Lord of the Dance' for the first hymn.

20

Jottings

Brenda Dawson

Miss Brenda Dawson, a Primary School Headmistress, was admitted to St. Christopher's on March 6th, 1986. These are some of her poems, written while she was a patient.

My big toe twiddled all by itself
A nerve made it jump in the air.
I wish it would move under my control
For I can't take it anywhere.

Two paralysed legs stretch down the bed,
The left moves a little but not the right.
I exercise just like the physio said.
One day it will move, it might.

Waves of envy flow through me
As people walk past my door.
I hate their legs and nimble feet
I want to scream and roar.

Frustration builds up, dependence reigns,
I can't reach my books or my pens.
Shall I push the buzzer and call in the staff
Or wait till their meeting ends?

BD, April 12th, 1986

Be Not Dismayed

'Be not dismayed,' the psalmist said.
Easier said than done.
I am dismayed, deep into my mind,
I'm frightened, I'm nervous,
My heart's all aflutter,
The future looks bleak and forlorn.
What sort of life can it possibly hold
Dependent on others for all that I need?

My life is reduced in quantity,
Or is this illusion and lies?
It's changed so much I just can't adjust
To no work, no flat, no legs that walk.
And how do I measure quality?
Is that as it was before?
Can you measure your life by what you do?
No, that is illusion, it cannot be true.

'Be not dismayed,' the psalmist said.
Life just goes on, day follows day
Transformed it may be, narrow and tight,
But its depth never varies
And its height is all right.
So what must I do to find value in life?
Attend to the Lord, he will show me the way.
Attend to the Lord, all the live-long day.

BD, April 16th, 1986

This is for real!
It's not, it can't be!
But it's six months now
And still I hope it is a dream.

How can my mind confound my reason so?
My intelligence takes second place to my emotions.
This is no game, it is for real.

Pins and needles
From T7 down
I've got pins and needles
Lack of sensation
Muscles that sleep
From T7 down
I'm a dangling clown!

BD, April 26th, 1986

Rugby Ward

Dame Julian of Norwich
Chose to herself a cell
Wherein to worship God
Removed from kith and kin
But the world pressed in.

Julian saw no split
Between the world and God.
In my cell could I respond like this?
Julian in her cell was free
But this choice was made for me.

Could I make my cell throb
With such intensity of life
As she did hers?
Could I commune with my Creator force,
Assist with life's creative course?

Love of God was Julian's motivating force,
I feel a fight within,

Both love and anger trouble me,
How could such motivation
Inspire this cell-like situation?

BD, May 2nd, 1986

Had a Good Day?

What is enjoyment in this cell-like situation?
Is it appreciation of each small glory?
The flash of sunlight on a flower.
The song on the lips of a nurse.
The letter from a friend, telephone calls.
A sudden, joyful synchronicity of thoughts or
A glimpse of a child playing,
Absorbed in its fantasy,
A bird singing outside in the garden.
All show forth the Glory of God
And in gratitude I can respond in thankfulness.
But first I have to learn
To recognise the moment of enjoyment.

BD, May 4th, 1986

If only I had more time I would . . .
Well, now I have, and I can't . . .

I need an aim well defined,
Printed out, pinned upon the wall.

Life has not stopped, I do have time
But what shall I do with it?

How will I account at the end of time
For this period of my life?

Since I cannot produce a tangible, visible product,
Can I produce an intangible, invisible one?

Could I attempt to straighten out my inner life,
Uncover the blueprint Christ intended.

While I fight this disease and handicap, perhaps
This is my time to be, not do.

BD, May 8th, 1986

Forgiveness

God, you need to ask my forgiveness.
Your world is full of mistakes.
Some cells, like weeds in the garden
Are growing in the wrong place.
And we your children
Have polluted our environment.
Why did you let it happen God?
We prayed with faith, hope, love,
We perceived no change in our bodies or environment,
We are made sick by your world.
God you need to ask my forgiveness.
Was this why you sent your Son?

BD, May 11th, 1986

Assembly Rainbow

I used to look at you and see
All the colours of the rainbow
Looking up at me.
Red hair and black,
Blue eyes and green.
Pink jeans, yellow tops,
All the colours I've ever seen.

Your lovely faces were smiling brightly
Ready to start the day.
Here to learn, to work and play.
Reading and writing,
Counting and painting,
Letters written for Miss Dawson
To cheer her day along.

I wish I could send you a rainbow,
All rolled up for a rainy day.
They speak of great beauty
And promise of love.
Without rainbows, life would be a sadder place
I love the rainbow letters you send me.

BD, June 13th, 1986

Miss Dawson in her Wheelchair

Look out! Look out!
She's coming around this way.
Dashing along between the beds,
Mind your toes,
Tuck in your heads,
It's Dare Devil Dawson
In her wheelie chair.
Away to the lifts,
Down to the garden,
Wheelie around the pond.
Nurses chasing,
Joining in the fun.
Back upstairs to her bed, relaxing
Looking as good as gold.
Miss Dawson doing a wheelie?
Never!
Must have been someone else!

BD, June 22nd, 1986

A Sunny Afternoon

Sitting in the sunshine
Looking at the pond.
Monet's water lilies,
Chinese golden carp,
Golden Iris waving,
Tinkling water sounds.
Everything oozing lifewards
In St. Christopher's Hospice grounds.

Amongst the trees and flowers
The bright umbrellas and chairs,
Beautiful people are sitting
Enjoying the peaceful hours.
Actively waiting for life.
Visitors come with flowers and fruit
And love is shared around between sick and well
In St. Christopher's Hospice grounds.

BD, June 28th, 1986

Through a Glass Darkly

It's lucky our eyes look outward
We can't see how we look
Without mirrors.
As our bodies diminish
Or lose their shape
It's the others who see it.
We feel its limitations.
How do we look in their eyes?
Does it hurt our family and friends
To see us changed so much?
As we move lifewards
So we become transformed.
Through our dark internal glass we see clearly
But the eyes of our friends cloud over.

In their concern they recall us
As we used to be, loving and alive.
But they seem unable to see the new life
Rising within us.

BD, June 28th, 1986

Brenda Dawson died on July 26th, 1986.

21

Night-time

Wendy Letham

Wendy Letham was a Staff Nurse at St. Christopher's
from April 15th, 1985 to June 21st, 1987, and is now a
Ward Sister at a near-by hospital.

Nights can be lonely and fearful when death is near. Imagination has free reign. Time hangs heavy.

Each minute with a dying loved one is precious, yet those same minutes seem never ending when you are waiting for a life to end.

The atmosphere of the place is different at night. Each sound is distinct from the next, startling in clarity, its meaning distorted and somehow more ominous. Ill people seem much more vulnerable. There are fourteen of them here in this ward: some are imminently dying, but others can still enjoy life and activity of one kind or another. There are others here, too, families who watch over loved ones, accompanying them through the darkness, clustering in armchairs around dimly-lit beds, talking in whispers, lapsing into stillness, creeping away in stockinged feet to dispel the tension of waiting. It was on such a night that George died. This is the story of his death. The memory of it will always linger in the minds of those who shared that time with him.

George had really fought this illness. But the cancer had assaulted his body, which was now gaunt and yellow from its effects. Despite his weakness George could still walk to the bathroom and back, even on the day before his death. In his disciplined determination, he measured every effort so as to squeeze the final drops of life from his tired body. A weaker man might have given up and let go of life months earlier, but not so George. Determination had been sustaining him and now made it difficult to break the momentum. This became particularly evident during the night before he died.

The first that George's son knew of the imminence of his father's death was when their family doctor handed him the completed referral form for the Hospice in an unsealed envelope. James of course read it. The estimated duration of life was '1–2 weeks'. Surely this could not be true? He could not make sense of this shocking information. Dad had been ill for so long – three years now. Could it end so soon? Somehow James had imagined his father would carry on indefinitely, weak though he was. They had all got used to his frail appearance. Perhaps the GP had got it wrong? Having had no warning from him, the family had presumed that things were going well. At the age of 21, James could not handle this turn of events. When his father had been admitted to the Hospice, he found it difficult to visit him and impossible to sit with him, often staying apart from the rest of the family at visiting times.

Unlike James, his sister Karen had not, in fact, been surprised at the way things were going. She was a little older, 25 and had been quietly watching her father's health deteriorating with frightening speed in the last few weeks. She was particularly close to her mother and both women were aware that, hard as he had fought, George's fierce will to survive had outstripped the capacity of his now enfeebled body. That he might soon die was a real possibility to them both. Grey shadows around Karen's eyes betrayed long nights made sleepless by concern for the rest of her family.

Their mother, Sarah, was much better prepared for George's death than either James or Karen imagined. As a family, they had never discussed the inevitable but instead had concentrated on enjoying as much as possible the two years since George had retired from work. Husband and wife had joined the National Trust, spending many weekends and days out together, appreciating every friend and experience in a new light. The family had only moved down to London from their native Scotland four years ago when George had been transferred to the Metropolitan Police force. At that time he had been a fit 47-year-old. Even up until six months before he came to the Hospice he had been able to enjoy a round of golf with his godson, John, in the sunshine of an Edinburgh October.

The primary cancer in George's bowel had been removed but its spread to the liver was now causing most of his many physical problems. He had only just completed another course of chemotherapy when he had taken the decision to come into the Hospice. He had begun to agree that he was dying, but considered that there was still fighting to be done. His eyes were the only part of him that still seemed full of life. Limbs and chest were wasted, the face gaunt and hollow, the skin yellow and dull. Every physical effort was made at a cost and the movements were painfully slow and measured. When he slept his features looked skull-like and it was a relief when he woke and his bright blue eyes radiated the flame of life still burning strongly within.

He was gently spoken and enquiring about each new aspect of treatment, remaining firmly in control but gradually relaxing his defences as he settled into Hospice life. Staff warmed to his quiet charm and evident dignity and it was easy to take into their hearts the members of his family, as onlookers were moved not only by George's resilience but also the care the family showed to each other. He had brought his Bible with him and although he did not speak much of his faith, it was solid and constant. Their minister came to visit them while George was in the Hospice, bringing considerable comfort to Sarah and Karen in particular, who found themselves more able to speak out their fears to a familiar friend than to the staff who were still relative strangers.

Yet George was not ready to die. Every small action was a struggle to maintain normality, but he was gradually losing the battle and with it his grip on life. For some days he managed to keep up this pretence in front of his family, struggling to maintain a façade of normality for their sakes, although they could hardly bear to watch him trying to turn back what they now felt certain was quite inevitable.

Then, one evening the transition occurred and the whole family were together around George's bed, weeping and embracing, one comforting the other, able for once to share their profound sadness among themselves, no one needing any longer to keep up a brave face. Now James was able to get close to his father again, Karen no longer needed to appear the strong one and Sarah was able to express some of her emotion in front of her children, obviously realistic about the future, her own mind much eased by the sight of her children grieving thus. The truth had been shared and was as a result much less frightening.

There was more heartache to come when George said he would still carry on fighting, despite all that had just been shared. He meant it to reassure them but they found no comfort in the words.

The next morning, however, George had changed his mind a little more. He confided to the doctor that he could now accept that he was going to die very soon. The rest of the family were never to hear him say this, although the doctor was able to relay it to them when they visited later that day. It was as if George had granted permission that he should now die. Neither James nor Karen, realising this, wished to be present at the death so they went home that evening leaving only Sarah and godson John who would stay with George to face whatever would happen next. Sarah was filled with indecision whether to go or to stay. Suddenly, every minute had become precious. George's physical condition had lately deteriorated further: all day long he had felt nauseated, he had twice vomited blood and had spent the day lying on his bed drifting in and out of an exhausted restless sleep. The discomfort in his abdomen was gradually increasing and he was finding it difficult to keep down the analgesic and anti-emetic medicines he badly needed. Consequently, he had not hàd the benefit of them but he was still refusing to have his medication by injection, seeing this as a sign of further deterioration and loss of control.

Sarah asked the staff for advice whether to stay or not, asking if they now thought he would die that night. She was urged to stay a little longer, though somehow no one could imagine that George's fierce fight for life could actually come to an end.

When the night staff arrived to take over from the late shift, George was sleeping, made more drowsy by the side-effects of medication given for nausea. The figure lying there on the bed bore no resemblance to the photograph of him, taken at his silver wedding celebrations only a year earlier, which stood on the bedside locker. Now, he looked less than alive.

At 9 p.m. he was incontinent for the first time. As he was cleaned and the bed linen changed, he was obviously feeling very sick, yet was too weak and tired to vomit. He could only get comfortable by lying on his back, shoulders slightly propped up, abdomen taut and distended. There now seemed little chance that oral medication would stay down, or if it did that it would be absorbed, so the nurse tried to explain to him the real need for him to accept medication by injection. If he refused, she feared that his pain and sickness would get far beyond the capacity for control. Thankfully, he agreed, making the task of controlling his symptoms through the long night ahead less daunting for those charged with his care. In fact, this agreement was the last time he spoke to anyone.

He went back to sleep, Sarah in an armchair at the bedside. However, even sleep did not seem to bring rest. He groaned and grimaced as if he were struggling with something in his sleep but he could not be woken. Was it just his physical discomfort causing this or could it be some mental or spiritual battle?

Seeing that he would not wake again, Sarah decided to stay with him through the night. Staff tried gently to explain that it could all happen very quickly now. The night wore on. From time to time Sarah left the bedside to stretch her legs, seeming calm and apparently not sharing the nurse's considerable concern about his restlessness which had so far not been reached by medication. It seemed as though George was undergoing inner torment, but who could say? At least Sarah did not seem unduly distressed by it. Silent prayers went up for God to free him from his conflict which seemed to have gone on for so long. It was all they could do to help him. At 4 a.m., for the first time that night, the injection (or perhaps the prayers) seemed to give George some relief and he lay quietly, breathing more easily. The grey light of dawn seeped through the curtains at 6 a.m. While Sarah had a cup of tea, the nurses changed his pyjamas again. He was turned on to his right side; now he was relaxed and did not resist their efforts. The breathing was quiet at last and the body no longer stiff or awkward, but no pulse could be felt in the wrist.

Sarah returned and could see straight away that something had changed. For half an hour the three of them stayed motionless, soaking up the feeling of peace which was almost tangible, like balm after the rawness and tension of the vigil. The night had been full of fear but with the dawn seemed to have come peace at last.

Daylight now streamed in through the windows. Suddenly the breathing changed and became irregular. The nurse hurried to fetch John who had been sleeping in the room next door. Fuddled by sleep, he followed her urgent beckoning to George's bedside.

Although George had not uttered a word all night, they heard his voice now cut through the silence. No words could be distinguished but it was unmistakably his voice, not merely a groan, sigh or whisper. It sounded like an expression of deep contentment or even of reconciliation, though it was unclear to whom it was addressed. He took two short breaths, then it was over. The moment had passed and George had died.

'Father into your hands I commend my spirit.'

The four figures stayed still for several minutes as the truth gradually sank into the tired minds of those who had watched, who had waited and who had finally been rewarded.

Then, Sarah began to reminisce, recalling the good times she and George had shared together. The recollections were warm with affection and under their influence the three who had watched began to relax. The uncertainty was over and the tension gone. Life filtered back into them with the advent of the day.

George was only in the Hospice for ten days but it would seem that his last struggle was a final fight, in character, and mental rather than physical. However, many patients and families continue to fear that if morphine is started early it will 'lose its effect'. The reverse is nearer the truth, for good pain control throughout a terminal illness makes the use of high-level opioids less likely. The really intractable pain, seen occasionally at the end of life, is often preceded by months of inadequate control leading to depression, anger and fear.

It also seems right in this context to add a relevant part of Judge Patrick Devlin's summing up in the trial of Dr John Bodkin Adams:

If the first purpose of medicine, the restoration of health, can no longer be achieved, there is still much for a doctor to do, and he is entitled to do all that is proper and necessary to relieve pain and suffering, even if the measures he takes may incidentally shorten life. This is not because there is a special defence for medical men but because no act is murder which does not cause death. We are not dealing here with the philosophical or technical cause, but with the commonsense cause. The cause of death is the illness or the injury, and the proper medical treatment that is administered and that has an incidental effect on determining the exact moment of death is not the cause of death in any sensible use of the term. But . . . no doctor, nor any man, no more in the case of the dying than of the healthy, has the right deliberately to cut the thread of life.

22

Being Quiet Together

Cicely Saunders

Derek Williams was admitted to the Hospice on a Thursday in January 1987. His wife had cared for him as motor neurone disease gradually took away all his powers of movement until the physical effort became too much even for her determination. His problems included, as he said, 'poor nights due to fears of breathlessness and choking, discomfort and immobility'. They were both exhausted. After just one night in the ward he reported that he had only woken once and had not slept so well for over a month.

The next day he settled in well, he was assessed by the physiotherapist, and his wife continued part of his care herself. He began to make friends.

I met him on the Saturday when the medication that had helped his breathlessness at night was obviously going to be needed during the day as well. This helped the remaining discomfort and he continued to sleep better and have more ease in the time he spent with his visiting family.

Sunday was a full day. He had a bath, he attended the Free Church Service with several members of the family. A lay reader himself, he took a full part in the congregation. He also received Communion in the ward.

That lunchtime his three-months-old grandchild was visiting and joined in a little liquidised food.

Later he sent the rest of the family away and asked his wife to fetch their dog. They were peacefully there with him until he died quietly in the early hours of Monday morning.

Two weeks later Mrs Williams wrote to me:

Dear Dame Cicely

May I, through you, send my love and thanks to the staff at St. Christopher's who helped to make Derek's last weekend such a joyous and comforting one.

As the hours passed it became clear to me that if he had been at home, I could not have managed on my own – so, unhampered by the physical caring, we could be quiet *together*. At home, involved in the daily caring routine I would have missed these precious, peaceful last hours.

I've had over 200 letters, all of which are lovely and very touching. Each in its own way says the same thing: that he was an upright, totally honest, Christian man.

One letter says 'He was a valiant soldier in the service of the Lord' and I know that this was so.

Derek could not have been anywhere more fitting than St. Christopher's. That he was able to attend Chapel and take Communion gave him peace and a blessing.

I send love and blessings to you all.

In gratitude,
Kitty Williams

St. Christopher's

like most hospice units, relies extensively on donations to support its work. National Health Service funding covers less than half its needs. St. Christopher's is very grateful to the general public, and particularly to the local community, for the support which has made its continued development possible.

Contributions may be sent to:
The Administrator
St. Christopher's Hospice
51–59 Lawrie Park Road
London SE26 6DZ

BLESSINGS

Mary Craig

When her second child was born with a rare disease, Mary Craig was overwhelmed by the problems of caring for someone too handicapped even to know her. But one day she volunteered for a week's work at a home for concentration camp survivors. Here, among people who were joyful in spite of their suffering, Mary Craig found the peace and strength that enabled her to accept her life. With a growing understanding of the Christian faith, she came to see God's love and purpose for her and her family, even when tragedy struck a second time.

'The most moving book I have come across in years. I believe it will strike a responsive chord in the hearts of men and women everywhere.' *Morris West*

'A beautiful book that will bring comfort and understanding to anyone who is suffering, bereaved or just sad . . . I beg you to read it.' *Sunday Express*

'This book blossoms. It captivates. It flows like a lovely river . . . Do not miss it.' *Church Times*

ALONE

Katie Wiebe

'A deeply moving book, rich in honesty, practicality and scriptural good sense. A book of preparation for widowhood as well as a balm to those in the midst of it. I heartily recommend this book.'

Elizabeth-Ann Horsford

On November 17, 1962, Katie Wiebe's life changed course. Her secure role as a wife and mother was shattered. Widowhood changed the road signs, and together with her four young children she was sent down a new path. She found herself alone in a strange new community, stripped of her identity.

This unique and moving story is Wiebe's account of how she found the strength to survive the loneliness and loss of identity, the practical and emotional consequences of widowhood. Challenged to surrender security in earthly things, such as finances, possessions and even the role of the husbandless woman, Wiebe learned to place her trust in God, and through a leap of faith, to move on. Turning her eyes outward and to a new career, the author found life regained a sense of meaning.

Katie Wiebe is a well-known writer and conference speaker in the States, where she is also an associate professor of English and journalism.

CICELY SAUNDERS

Shirley du Boulay

Cicely Saunders belongs to that small but illustrious band of Englishwomen who have left a permanent impress on the history of their times. Dame Cicely's cause has been the care of the dying, and this book tells the story of the revolution she has inspired, both in the medical treatment of the dying, and in the nursing profession's understanding of their personal dignity and individual needs. She has been called 'the woman who changed the face of death'.

Shirley du Boulay is best known as a radio and TV producer, first on *Woman's Hour* and then with the Religious Programmes department of BBC TV. Now a freelance, she lives in Oxfordshire with her husband, John Harriott.